MAKING FR
with NUMBERS

Let learning Multiplication Facts teach you Math

Creative Strategies

Creative Worksheets

Edric Cane
Author, *Teaching to Intuition*

Updated Version

ISBN 978-0-916785-24-6

Check *MakingFriendswithNumbers.com* for additional material and suggestions
         as well as free shipping and quantity discount options.
Check also *TeachingtoIntuition.com* and *GrowyourBrain.education*.
Check, like, comment, sign-on to *YouTube Edric Cane* for growing collection of videos.

For comments and feedback, email: *edricmath@gmail.com*

10   9   8   7   6   5   4   3   2

Reviews on Amazon

A great supplement to the math we do. *My 10 year old son LOVES this book. It's a great supplement to the math that we do and it's more "fun" than some of the other things.* *Samantha Jacokes.*

A great tool for practice. *My daughter and I really enjoyed using this workbook this last school year. It has several creative ways to get to know numbers and their relationships. We will finish it this fall.* *Homeworker.*

The best workbook ever created. *Really helped my kids get away from skip counting. In only three weeks they have really memorized multiplication facts and enjoy doing the sheets.* *Joy.*

Excellent resource for Learning Multiplication Through Games and Practice. *My 8-yo son absolutely LOVED it. He'd complain about all the rest of his school work, but he couldn't wait to work in this each day. (In fact, I recently overhead him telling his younger sister that he wishes he could do it again!)* *O.A.*

It works! Numbers can be friends! *Great alternative practice to drilling multiplication. Truly allowed my child to play with numbers and become friends with them, rather (than) sworn enemies. Much of it is self-checking.* *C. Gustafson.*

Connections

A significant number of students and adults readily admit that they don't like math. I don't blame them. I too would share their dislike if math for me was the clutter of memorized rules and procedures that they usually understand as knowing math.

Mathematics is a thinking activity. Mathematical knowledge itself is a thinking activity. And yet, an indispensable segment of early math instruction focuses on teaching essential addition and multiplication facts. If presented mostly as something that just needs to be memorized, they imprint on the mind a completely wrong idea of what math represents and a negative emotional connection with the subject that many will never shake off. **Making Friends with Numbers** seeks to be an alternative.

Instead of an early burden, learning math facts can be an opportunity to discover math as a thinking process. Yes, memory is important, but it can be just one dimension in a rich network of connections, patterns, understandings and applications. Learning multiplication facts can reveal the structure and interaction of factors and develop number-sense.

Connections give memory a handle on a fact; they help the memorizing process and later offer a discreet background confirmation to the promptings of memory. Patterns mean that learning one fact helps learn and practice other facts within the same pattern. I want student to know $5 \times 8 = 40$. Great. But seeing and understanding the double/half connection between 8 and the 4 of 40 makes it easier for students to know $5 \times 9 = 45$ as they see 45 as one half of 90. It may at some later stage quite naturally expand to knowing that $5 \times 24 = 120$ as 12 is recognized as one half of 24. A web of overlapping connections of different kinds builds a quality of knowledge that stands in contrast to the brain-dead knowledge of individual facts each separately entrusted to memory.

In very concrete ways, **Making Friends with Numbers** uses the need to master essential facts as a unique opportunity to introduce mathematics as a creative and thinking activity.

Resources

MakingFriendswithNumbers.com.

Check for updates, sample answer keys for worksheets and additional material.

YouTube Edric Cane

Check, like, comment, subscribe (for free) to this **YouTube** channel.

Also by Edric Cane:

Grow your Brain, a mostly oral approach to a Great Start in Math.

What **Making Friends with Numbers** is for multiplication facts, **Grow your Brain** is for addition facts and also for other 1st and 2nd grade material. But it does so in a very different way. It is only for parents/teachers and proposes short dialogs and simple activities that help children discover and learn. For a sample, check YouTube video **Itsy Bitsy Spider and Addition Facts.**

Teaching to Intuition, Mathematics.

Teaching to Intuition is written for those who teach. It uses examples from Elementary and Middle School material only. It develops an approach to what it means to teach, learn and know math that builds on what students already know through their intuitive understanding of the world they experience. The approach appeals to students naturally inclined to mathematics and also to those who never catch on, who fall on the wrong side of the achievement gap and readily admit that they don't like math. In very concrete ways, **Teaching to Intuition** proposes an alternative that seeks to open wide to all the path to basic numeracy and to the STEM professions of the future.

> *"Edric's book is absolutely outstanding. His insight into kids' mental processes, and his techniques for building bridges between real-world experience and math processing are something pretty close to a paradigm shift. AND he knows how to write clearly, simply, conversationally."*
> Howard and Marion Brady.
> Educators, authors. *What's Worth Learning.*

> *"We recommend Edric Cane's book Teaching to Intuition as an excellent source for how mathematics should be learned. This is mainly for elementary mathematics, but the principles hold for all levels."*
> Fred Krogh, Principal mathematician (Ret.),
> NASA's Jet Propulsion Laboratory, Pasadena, CA.

How to use
Making Friends with Numbers

> **Worksheets are self-explanatory.**
> **Students can turn to the first page and get started.**

Active parent/teacher participation

Students can open the book and work on their own, but parents/teachers are strongly encouraged to take an active role in the learning process. Suggestions for doing so are included in brief teacher frames on different worksheets and as **Guided Discovery** pages. These are mostly questions for parents/teachers to ask that help students discover the material before it is assigned. Parents/teachers can also ask students to explain the model and solve orally the first examples. The worksheets become a written confirmation and practice of what is already essentially understood. Both students and parents/teachers can agree to cooperate in the discovering and learning process.

No need to grade or correct

The worksheets are learning tools, not a test of knowledge. There is no need to correct them. A quick check that the material is understood and that there are no systematic errors is all that is needed. Everything is seen multiple times and an occasional error is not that important. Check *MakingFriendswithNumbers.com* for sample answer keys to corrected worksheets.

A cumulative process

The material is presented in a cumulative process. What is seen in the early pages is reviewed and practiced multiple times in other worksheets. Students spend some time on multiples of 5 or 9, and all subsequent worksheets provide continued practice on those facts.

Learning much more than facts

For most worksheets, the thinking and learning that take place before the first number is written down is more important than the writing that follows. That may not come naturally to students. It implies taking time to understand. But, as they learn facts, students will develop number-sense in ways that prepare them for a smooth transition to algebra. Most importantly, they will experience mathematics as a thinking activity.

36 Essential Facts

31 numbers representing
36 essential facts from 2 × 2 to 9 × 9.

4	
6	
8	
9	
10	
12	12
14	
15	
16	16
18	18
20	
21	
24	24
25	
27	
28	
30	
32	
35	
36	36
40	
42	
45	
48	
49	
54	
56	
63	
64	
72	
81	

Times Square

1	2	3	4	5	6	7	8	9
2	4	6	8	10	12	14	16	18
3	6	9	12	15	18	21	24	27
4	8	12	16	20	24	28	32	36
5	10	15	20	25	30	35	40	45
6	12	18	24	30	36	42	48	54
7	14	21	28	35	42	49	56	63
8	16	24	32	40	48	56	64	72
9	18	27	36	45	54	63	72	81

Contents

Level 1: Multiples of 2, 5, 9: that's already 21 facts.

Level 2: The remaining 15 facts.

Level 3: Continued Practice. Prime Factors, Greatest Common Factors, Least Common Multiples, etc.

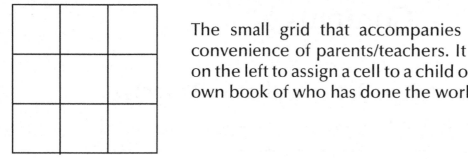

The small grid that accompanies each worksheet is for the convenience of parents/teachers. It allows them to use the grid on the left to assign a cell to a child or class and keep track in their own book of who has done the worksheet.

Multiply these numbers by 10 by adding one zero.

2____   15____   871____   34____   10____   4____

247____   1____   7____   3____   500____   47____

Multiply these numbers by 100 by adding two zeros.

2____   15____   87____   34____   10____   4____

How many zeros?

Multiply these numbers by 1,000.

6_____   28_____   47_____   14_____   8_____

Divide these numbers by 10 by crossing out:

1370   300   1000   120

50   170   6250   930

Frames such as this one mark a parent/teacher corner. They include brief suggestions, precautions, options for the use of the worksheet, as well as prompts or questions that the parent/teacher can ask even before students look at the worksheet. With or without framed suggestions, **most worksheets will benefit greatly from active parent/teacher participation,** allowing the written practice to become a confirmation and application of what has just been explored in a dynamic dialog with students.

Here, for instance, very simple prompts using different numbers can help students discover the essential concept. Students are not told to add one or more zeros, but are helped as needed to make the discovery themselves: *"Here's a 2. What can you do to that number to make it 10 times larger?"* Once discovered and practiced orally and with numbers written on a board or scratch paper, the worksheet itself becomes an independent confirmation. (See **Place Value, Digits in Motion** video at *YouTube.com*. Search: Edric Cane.)

Review Addition Facts

It doesn't make much sense to learn multiplication facts if you don't know how to add. So we assume students know essential addition facts. Still, the next few worksheets are an opportunity for a quick review of those facts. If not needed, these worksheets can be skipped, but we suggest that students who essentially know the material still run through them in a couple of sessions. (See **Grow your Brain** for addition facts.)

Each domino represents two numbers and their sum. Show the math as in model.

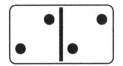

$$2 + 2 = 4$$

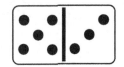

$$5 + 3 = 8$$

Always study and understand model answers.

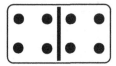

_____

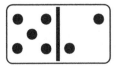

_____

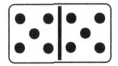

_____

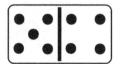

_____

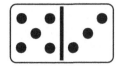

_____

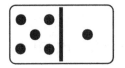

_____

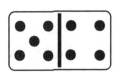

_____

1 less than 10.
5 + 4 = 9.

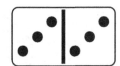

_____

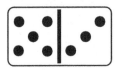

_____

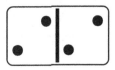

_____

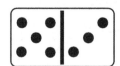

_____

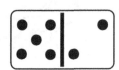

_____

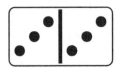

_____

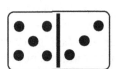

_____

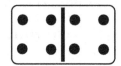

_____

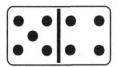

_____

Review Addition Facts

Add as in model:

Where does the 2 of 12 come from?

[domino] = 7	[domino] = ___	[domino] = ___
[domino] = 7	[domino] = ___	[domino] = ___
10 + 4 = 14	___ + ___ = ___	___ + ___ = ___

[domino] = ___	[domino] = ___	[domino] = ___
[domino] = ___	[domino] = ___	[domino] = ___
___ + ___ = ___	___ + ___ = ___	___ + ___ = ___

[domino] = ___	[domino] = ___	[domino] = ___
[domino] = ___	[domino] = ___	[domino] = ___
___ + ___ = ___	___ + ___ = ___	___ + ___ = ___

[domino] = ___	[domino] = ___	[domino] = ___
[domino] = ___	[domino] = ___	[domino] = ___
___ + ___ = ___	___ + ___ = ___	___ + ___ = ___

Add as in model:

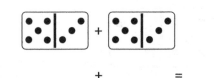

□ + □ 6 + 6 = **12**	□ + □ _____ + _____ = _____

> 6 = 5 + 1
> So: 2 × 6 = 10 + _____

□ + □
_____ + _____ = _____

□ + □
_____ + _____ = _____

□ + □
_____ + _____ = _____

□ + □
_____ + _____ = _____

> 8 = 5 + 3
> So: 2 × 8 = 10 + _____

□ + □
_____ + _____ = _____

- -

□ + □
_____ + _____ = _____

□ + □
_____ + _____ = _____

□ + □
_____ + _____ = _____

□ + □
_____ + _____ = _____

□ + □
_____ + _____ = _____

□ + □
_____ + _____ = _____

□ + □
_____ + _____ = _____

> 9 = 5 + 4
> So: 2 × 9 = _____ + _____

□ + □
_____ + _____ = _____

Factor Pairs

$2 \times 7 = 14$ So 2 and 7 are a **factor pair** of 14. $\underset{}{\overset{2}{\rule{0pt}{0pt}}}$ (14) $\overset{7}{\rule{0pt}{0pt}}$

Write a factor pair of each number as in model. Use only factors **from 2 to 10.**

$\overset{4}{\rule{0pt}{0pt}}$ (40) $\overset{10}{\rule{0pt}{0pt}}$ (8)   (12)   (18)   (10)

(6)   (16)   (70)   (14)   (60)

(50)   (4)   (18)   (100)   (90)

(16)   (12)   (14)   (20)   (18)

Find the pattern:

$2 \times 7 =$ 14

$20 \times 7 =$ 140

$20 \times 70 =$ 1,400

$200 \times 70 =$ 14,000

$20 \times 900 =$ 18,000

What's 2 × 9?   Why 3 zeros?

Apply:

$20 \times 80 =$ _____

$200 \times 90 =$ _____

$60 \times 200 =$ _____

$20 \times 20 =$ _____

$4 \times 2,000 =$ _____

What's 2 × 6?   How many zeros?

$20 \times 600 =$ _____

$40 \times 20 =$ _____

$900 \times 200 =$ _____

$20 \times 24 =$ _____

$20 \times 500 =$ _____

Why 4 zeros here?

Double/Half Pairs (1)

It is difficult to see 10 and not know that 5 is its half, or see 5 and not know that 10 is its double. Familiarity with double/half pairs such as 10/5, 6/3, 14/7 and others goes far beyond knowledge of "two times" facts.
- It establishes connections that help students with other multiplication facts.
- It builds number-sense that serves students well in math and in real life.
- It is part of what it means to *make friends with numbers*.

The sessions devoted here to double/half connections are crucial and time well spent.

Complete these double/half pairs as in model:

10	20	30	40	50	60	70	80	90	100
5	10	15	___	___	___	___	___	___	50

Double: 60	40	90	___	___	___	___	80	70	
Half: ___	___	___	50	15	25	45	___	___	

30	___	50	___	90	___	30	70	___	90
___	45	___	35	___	30	___	___	20	___

Additions:

16 + 16 is 2 more than 15 + 15.

$$15 + 15$$ $$16 + 16$$ $$35 + 35$$

$$45 + 45$$ $$30 + 30$$ $$25 + 25$$

Worksheets are static. In contrast, dialogs with students are dynamic. They allow us to add explanations when initial responses show they are needed. We can build up answers in stages in ways that have a greater impact than the fully-developed answer.

Example, with the parent/teacher writing down students' oral answers: *70 is 60 + 10, right?*

What's one half of 60? 30

What's one half of 10? 5

So what's one half of 70? 35

Tell me how that works with 90 (30, 50).

Vocabulary: Check that students are familiar with EVEN and ODD.

Even numbers end with Even digits 2, 4, 6, 8, or 0.

Odd numbers end with Odd digits 1, 3, 5, 7, 9.

Even numbers are divisible by 2. Odd numbers are not.

Draw links between double/half pairs. (Long hand or with a ruler.)
Draw two links for bolder bubbles.

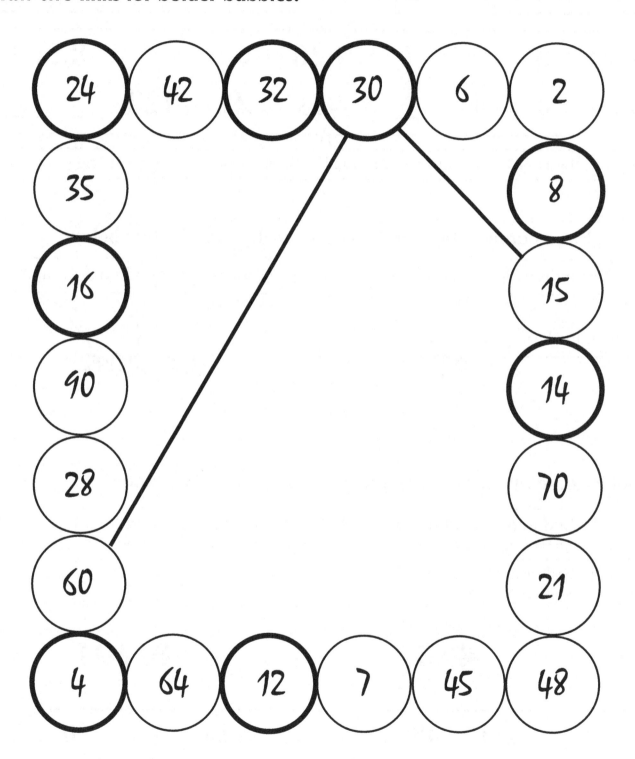

Trace again with finger or in color the path from 2 to 64 and from 6 to 48.

Complete these double/half pairs as in model:

When all the DIGITS of a number are EVEN, to find its half, divide each digit by 2:

Double:	8	2	6	826	42	____	8,602
Half:	4	1	____	413	21	123	_____

When all the DIGITS of a number are smaller than 5, double it by doubling each digit:

Divide these numbers by 2 orally and in writing on the line below:

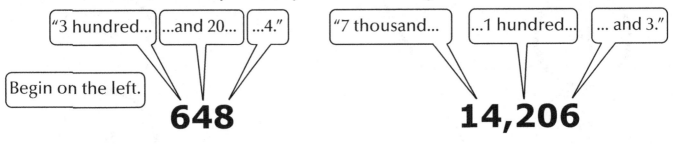

"3 hundred... | ...and 20... | ...4."

Begin on the left.

648

_____

"7 thousand... | ...1 hundred... | ... and 3."

14,206

_____

Double these numbers orally and in writing on the line above:

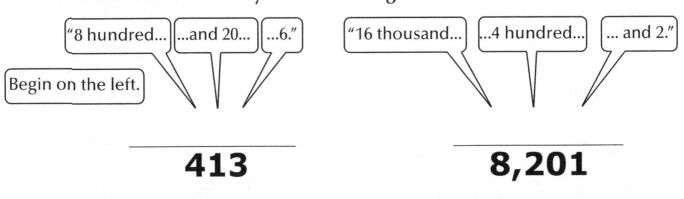

"8 hundred... | ...and 20... | ...6."

Begin on the left.

_____

413

"16 thousand... | ...4 hundred... | ... and 2."

_____

8,201

___	___	90	48	___	___	64	___	70	28
14	35	___	___	21	45	___	12	___	___

Double/Half Pairs (4)

Draw links between double/half pairs.
Draw two links for bolder bubbles.

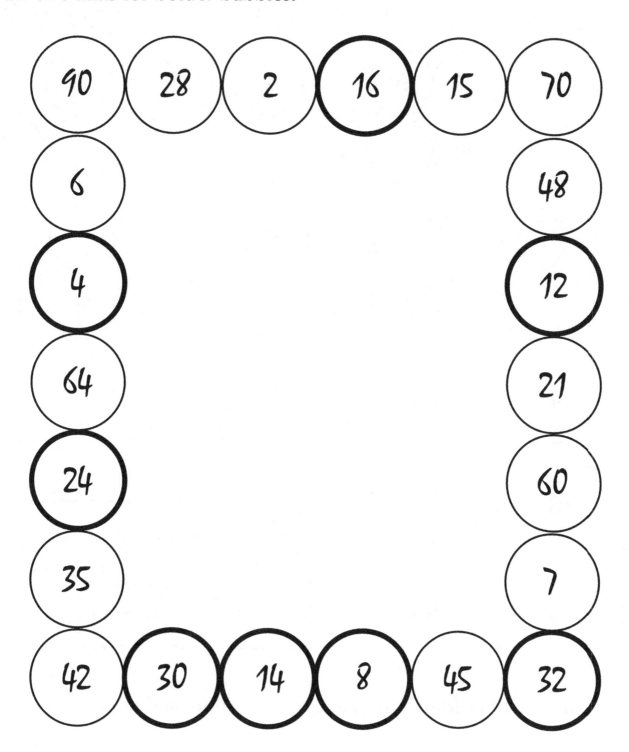

Trace again with finger or in color the path from 2 to 64 and from 6 to 48.

9

Complete the double/half pairs:

When doubles are multiples of 10:	Easy when 10s digit is even: 60 80 30 40	More difficult when it is odd: 70 90 30 35 45 15

Double: 40   60   ___   80   90   ___   70   ___

Half: 20   ___   25   ___   ___   15   ___   45

30   100   ___   ___   ___   90   50   ___   ___   ___   ___

___   ___   40   30   35   ___   ___   15   45   25

Double:	24	42	80	___	28	___	___	___	90
Half:	12	___	___	35	___	24	32	14	___

___	28	64	___	48
35	___	___	21	___

70	24	___	64
___	___	45	___	21

Congratulate students:
They now know how to divide by 2 mentally any number written with even digits only (and 0) and how to double any number written with digits 0, 1, 2, 3, 4.

Questions: *Write a long number using even digits only. Divide it by 2.*
Write a long number written with digits 1, 2, 3, 4, or 0 only. Double it.

Double each number from 2 to 128. Do it in writing and orally.

2	4	8	___	___	___	128
2	2×2	2×2×2	2×2×2×2	2×2×2×2×2	2×2×2×2×2×2	2×2×2×2×2×2×2

Complete these double/half pairs.

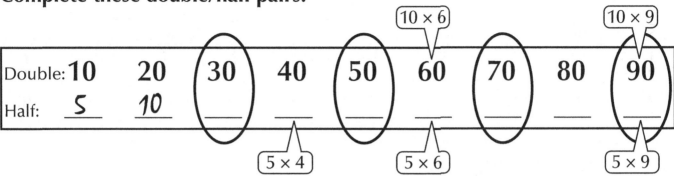

		10 × 6			10 × 9

Double: **10**　　**20**　（**30**）　**40**　（**50**）　**60**　（**70**）　**80**　（**90**）

Half: ___ **5** ___ 　 ___ **10** ___ 　（___）　___ 　（___）　___ 　（___）　___ 　（___）

5 × 4		5 × 6		5 × 9

Build orally on these double/half connections to help students discover how to multiply by 5:

What's 10 × 4? *(40)*　So what's 5 × 4? *(20)*　　What's 10 × 8 *(80)*　So what's 5 × 8? *(40)*
What's 10 × 7? *(70)*　So what's 5 × 7? *(35)*　　What's 10 × 9 *(90)*　So what's 5 × 9? *(45)*

Congratulations! Now you know how to multiply by 5.

- **5 is one half of 10.**
- **So multiplying by 5 is one half of multiplying by 10.**
- **To multiply by 5, multiply by 10 and divide by 2.**

Use the double/half pairs above to multiply by 5.

Double:　　10 × 4 = __40__　　10 × 7 = ____　　10 × 3 = ____

Half:　　　5 × 4 = __20__　　5 × 7 = ____　　5 × 3 = ____

10 × 6 = ____　　10 × 9 = ____　　10 × 8 = ____　　10 × 2 = ____

5 × 6 = ____　　5 × 9 = ____　　5 × 8 = ____　　5 × 2 = ____

5 × 4 = ____　　5 × 6 = ____　　5 × 5 = ____　　5 × 9 = ____

Count by fives, then by ones:

5	10	15	___	___	___	___	___	___	50
↓	↓	↓	↓	↓	↓	↓	↓	↓	↓
1	2	3	___	___	___	___	___	___	10

These numbers show that:

2 × 5 = _____   5 × 5 = _____   8 × 5 = _____

10 × 5 = _____   7 × 5 = _____   9 × 5 = _____

5 × 3 = _____   5 × 6 = _____   5 × 4 = _____

> Multiples of 5 end with _____ or _____.

Show factor pairs of these numbers. Use only factors from 2 to 10.

5 — (20) — 4   ___ — (15) — ___   ___ — (35) — ___   ___ — (45) — ___

___ — (12) — ___   5 — (40) — ___   ___ — (16) — ___   5 — (30) — ___

___ — (35) — ___   ___ — (18) — ___   5 — (20) — ___   ___ — (100) — ___

___ — (15) — ___   ___ — (25) — ___   ___ — (14) — ___   ___ — (35) — ___

You know how to multiply by 10.
You know how to divide by 2.
So you know how to multiply by 5.
Column after column, fill in the missing numbers:

- Check model.
- Understand the pattern.
- Explain it to parent/teacher.
- Take time to think.

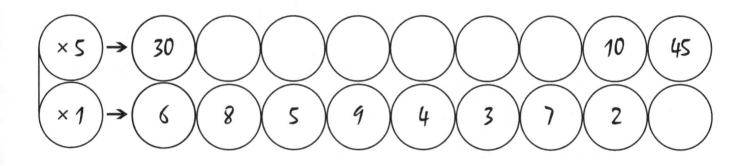

Double:
$\times 10 \rightarrow$ 40 | 30 | 80 | 70 | | | | 90

Half:
$\times 5 \rightarrow$ 20

7 × 5?
Divide 70 by 2.

$\times 1 \rightarrow$ 4 | 3 | | 7 | 6 | 8 | 5 | 9

$\times 5 \rightarrow$ 30 | | | | | | | 10 | 45
$\times 1 \rightarrow$ 6 | 8 | 5 | 9 | 4 | 3 | 7 | 2 |

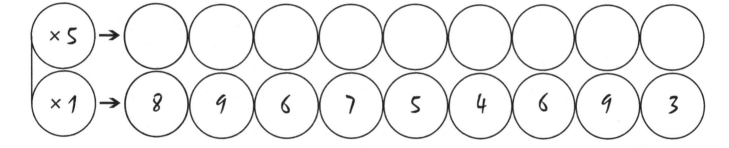

$\times 5 \rightarrow$
$\times 1 \rightarrow$ 8 | 9 | 6 | 7 | 5 | 4 | 6 | 9 | 3

Factor pairs. Use 5 as one of the factors:

5 — (30) —   5 — (45) —   5 — (15) —

(35) — 5   (20) — 5   (10) — 5

(45) —   (25) —   (35) —

This is a page that stresses understanding.

Multiplying by 5 is one half of multiplying by 10. Make sure students can explain and apply that relationship.

Challenge:
Can they apply it to multiplying 16 by 5? If not, why not?

If you know how to multiply by 10...

...and you know how to divide by 2:

You know how to multiply by 5.

Column after column, fill in the missing numbers:

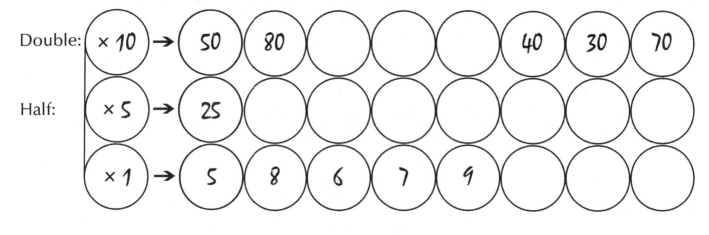

Double: × 10 → 50 80   40 30 70

Half: × 5 → 25

× 1 → 5 8 6 7 9

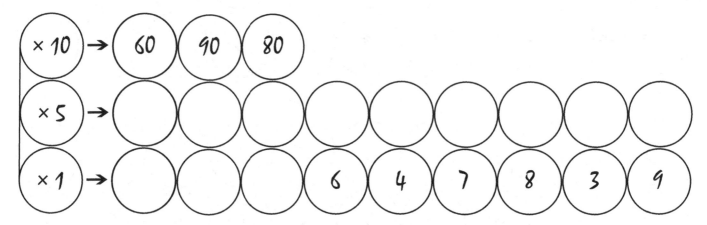

× 10 → 60 90 80

× 5 →

× 1 →   6 4 7 8 3 9

It is taken for granted that facts need to be reviewed and practiced over and over. Concepts and connections also need to be reviewed on multiple occasions. This is true of all those we will present in **Guided Discovery** pages or in other ways. Reminding students of the connection or the pattern should be the preferred alternative to reminding them only of the fact itself. Here, for instance, if a student later hesitates when having to multiply 12 by 5, we can ask a question about the corresponding multiple of 10: *"Well, what's 10 times 12?"* In most cases, there should be no need to add: *"And what's one half of 120?"*

Reviewing connections or patterns can be included at any time, in short or more extended versions, for no reason at all except the understanding that they are at the heart of what and how we want students to know. Teach a fact and the student knows a fact. Teach a pattern and the student knows even facts that have never been seen before: *"What's 5 times 864?"* We trust that at some point in the future, *"4,320"* will come easily to the thinking mind of a student or adult who sees 432 as one half of 864.

Multiples of 5 (5)

Here the numbers that you multiply by 5 are **EVEN**.
To multiply them by 5, you can first divide by 2; then multiply by 10.

$8 \div 2 = \underline{\ 4\ }$ $6 \div 2 = \underline{\quad}$ $16 \div 2 = \underline{\quad}$ $28 \div 2 = \underline{\quad}$

$8 \times 5 = \underline{\ 40\ }$ $6 \times 5 = \underline{\quad}$ $16 \times 5 = \underline{\ 80\ }$ $28 \times 5 = \underline{\quad}$

$14 \div 2 = \underline{\quad}$ $42 \div 2 = \underline{\quad}$ $4 \div 2 = \underline{\quad}$ $18 \div 2 = \underline{\quad}$

$14 \times 5 = \underline{\quad}$ $42 \times 5 = \underline{\quad}$ $4 \times 5 = \underline{\quad}$ $18 \times 5 = \underline{\quad}$

$10 \div 2 = \underline{\quad}$ $8 \div 2 = \underline{\quad}$

$10 \times 5 = \underline{\quad}$ $8 \times 5 = \underline{\quad}$

> By including larger numbers, we make it clear that students are practicing a pattern, thinking process, not drilling for pure memorization. They are just experiencing the process at this stage and should take their time to think.

Factor pairs.

$5 \times 8 = \underline{\quad}$ So ___ and ___ are a **factor pair** of 40. $\underline{\ 5\ }(40)\underline{\ 8\ }$

Write in the missing factor(s) in these factor pairs.

$\underline{\ 5\ }(20)\underline{\ 4\ }$ $\underline{\ 5\ }(30)\underline{\quad}$ $\underline{\ 5\ }(40)\underline{\quad}$ $\underline{\ 5\ }(50)\underline{\quad}$ $\underline{\ 5\ }(10)\underline{\quad}$

$\underline{\ 5\ }(15)\underline{\quad}$ $\underline{\ 5\ }(25)\underline{\quad}$ $\underline{\ 5\ }(35)\underline{\quad}$ $\underline{\ 5\ }(45)\underline{\quad}$ $\underline{\ 5\ }(30)\underline{\quad}$

$\underline{\quad}(16)\underline{\quad}$ $\underline{\quad}(12)\underline{\quad}$ $\underline{\quad}(18)\underline{\quad}$ $\underline{\quad}(14)\underline{\quad}$ $\underline{\quad}(45)\underline{\quad}$

Multiples of 5 (6)

Multiply each number by 5.

70 because 140 ÷ 2 = 70

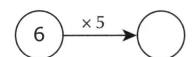

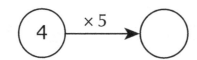

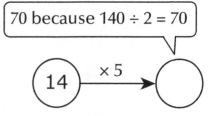

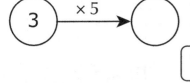

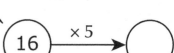

What's 90 ÷ 2?

What's 160 ÷ 2?

What's 16 ÷ 2?

Let me think.

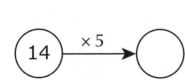

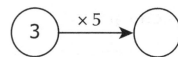

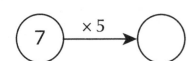

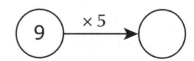

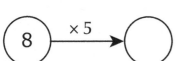

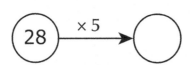

With even numbers you can think: "What's one half?" Then multiply by 10.

Multiples of 5 (7)

If the unit digit of a number is _____ or _____ that number is a multiple of 5.

14 of these numbers are multiples of 5.
1) Write in the factor 5 where it belongs. (ONLY 5, not the factor pair.)
2) Then write the factor pairs for all the numbers in the bubbles.

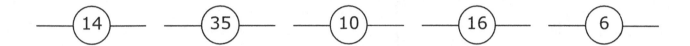

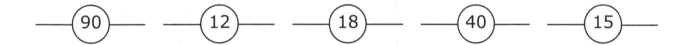

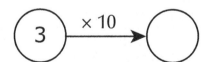
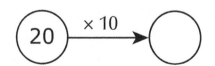
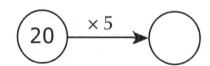

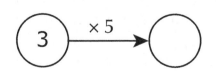

Why don't we include multiplying by 1 and 0?
At this stage, multiplying by 1 or 0 is a distraction.
It is not multiplying in the ordinary sense of the word.
Knowledge of essential facts such as 5 × 7 = 35, tells us about reality:
    Hamburgers cost $7.00 each. If I buy 5, that will cost me $ _____.
When multiplying by 1 or 0, reality speaks for itself:
    These drones cost $387.00 each. If I buy 1, I will pay $ _____
    If I don't buy any, I will spend $ _____ on drones.

The Basics

As soon as a fact family such as the 5-times facts has been studied, and while the facts, patterns and mental strategies are still fresh in memory, that family should be practiced orally multiple times. The lines on the back cover should help.

A finger moving up or down the line is a prompt that helps the mind focus on the fact, not on which number comes next. With the 5-times fact family in mind, as the finger moves down the line, students can do one of two things:

- Just give the corresponding product: "5, 10, 15, 20, 25, 30…" Lines on the back cover propose different sequences.
- More importantly, students can practice the sound and rhythm of a full oral statement:
  1 times 5, 5.
  2 times 5, 10.
  3 times 5, 15.
  4 times 5, 20...

Don't rush. As needed, take time to think.

A Strategy

To acquire memory of sound and rhythm:

Practice each fact family only up to the square of each number. Then, switch the order of the factors to still start with the smaller factor.

As your finger goes down the line, you first acquire the sound and rhythm of the 5-times facts but only up to $5 \times 5 = 25$:
  "3 times 5, 15."
  "4 times 5, 20."
  "5 times 5, 25."

Then, as the finger moves down to 6 on the line, you can stop or switch to saying "5" aloud first:
  "5 times 6, 30."
  "5 times 7, 35."
  "5 times 8, 40…"

This order makes it easier to learn and visualize multiplication facts. You still practice all 36 facts but only with the smaller factor first.

You can still practice the 5-times facts by running down the line from 1 to 10, but giving only the product: "5, 10, 15, 20, 25, 30…", not the full oral version. With the lines on the back cover, you can practice the facts in this way in a variety of orders.

By the end of level 2, once all essential facts have been studied, continued oral practice remains essential. Students who choose to practice fact families only to the square product may find that they can stop reviewing the 2-times, 3-times and 4-times fact families. That eliminates only from 2×2 to 4×4, six facts which are likely to be already familiar. Students may even choose to practice only fact families 6, 7, 8, 9 in this way, as multiples of 5 up to $5 \times 5 = 25$ are also likely to be well-known. (See Level 2, 2-29.)

Guided Discovery

Sometimes considered one of the more difficult, the 9-times fact family can be one of the easiest. Here, we invite parents/teachers to help students discover the patterns that make it so. A very simple conversation allows student to focus on patterns, one at a time. With no time pressure, no questions asked that students are not very likely to answer correctly, students are allowed to explore, discover and practice orally. Only then are worksheets assigned.

Sum of the Digits is 9 or a multiple of 9

> What's 9 + 9? You know how to add. Make a list of the first multiples of 9.

9   18   27   36   45   54   63   72   81   90

> As you add 9, what happens to the unit digits? To the 10s digits? Read them aloud.

> 18: What's 1 + 8? *(9)*   27: What's 2 + 7? *(9)*   36: What's 3 + 6? *(9)* ...
> What happens to the sum of the two digits? *(Doesn't change.)* Why?

One digit increases by 1. The other gets smaller by 1. The sum doesn't change.

> The Sum of the Digits is 9. That's true of all multiples of 9:
> Is 111,111,111 a multiple of 9? How can you tell?   *The sum of the digits is 9.*

> 2 + 7 is 9. Give me two numbers with these digits that are multiples of 9.   *27 and 72.*

> I give you a multiple of 9. Give me another multiple that uses the same two digits.
> 18...*(81)*   36...*(63)*   27...*(72)*   45...*(54)*   81...*(18)*

> I want a multiple of 9. Complete my prompt. No rush. Take time to think.
> Eighty... ? *(1. 81)*   Seventy... ? *(2. 72)*   Twenty...? *(7. 27)*   50...*(4. 54).*

10s digit is 1 less than the factor of 9:   8 × 9 begins with the 7 of 72.

> Show 3 × 9 on your list. What's the 10s digit? *(2).*   5 × 9: What's the 10s digit? *(4).*
> 8 × 9: What's the 10s digit? *(7).*   4 × 9: What's the 10s digit? *(3).* What's the pattern?

> If I say "7 × 9," you know it begins with 1 less than 7. So you can immediately say:
> "Sixty..." and then think of the unit digit "... *three.*" Let's try: 8 × 9? *(70...2)* 5 × 9? *(40...5)*

423: The digits are 4, 2, and 3. The SUM of the digits is 4 + 2 + 3 = 9

For all multiples of 9: The sum of the digits is always 9 (or a multiple of 9).

We know that 423 is a multiple of 9 because 4 + 2 + 3 = _____ .

111,111,111 is a multiple of 9 because the sum of the digits is _____ .

I take time to think and learn.

8 + 1 = 9. So __*81*__ and __*18*__ are multiples of 9.

6 + 3 = _____ So _____ and _____ are multiples of 9.

7 + 2 = _____ So _____ and _____ are multiples of 9.

4 + 5 = _____ So _____ and _____ are multiples of 9.

Write the unit's digit to make two-digit multiples of 9.

8*1*___ 7___ 6___ 5___ 4___ 3___

2___ 1___ 9___ 7___ 4___ 6___

7___ 8___ 3___ 5___ 6___ 2___

5___ 4___ 1___ 8___ 2___ 7___

This page helps students recognize multiples of 9. A student who knows 27 as a multiple of 9 is helped to also see 72 as a multiple of 9. 1 + 8 = 9, so 18, 81, and also 108 (12 × 9) are multiples of 9.

Oral preview or review: *"I say the first half of a 2-digit multiple of 9. You complete the number: Sixty...? (3); Forty...? (5); Twenty...? (7)..."*

Multiples of 9 (3)

Complete as in model.

7 × 9 begins with _6_, 1 less than 7:   7 × 9 = _63_

5 × 9 begins with ___, 1 less than 5:   5 × 9 = ___

8 × 9 begins with ___, 1 less than 8:   8 × 9 = ___

4 × 9 begins with ___, 1 less than 4:   4 × 9 = ___

2 × 9 begins with ___, 1 less than 2:   2 × 9 = ___

6 × 9 begins with ___, 1 less than 6:   6 × 9 = ___

3 × 9 begins with ___, 1 less than 3:   3 × 9 = ___

8 × 9 begins with ___: 8 × 9 = ___

4 × 9 begins with ___: 4 × 9 = ___

9 × 9 begins with ___: 9 × 9 = ___

6 × 9 begins with ___: 6 × 9 = ___

8 × 9 begins with ___: 8 × 9 = ___

One less:

8 × 9 = 72 = 8 × 9

One more:

Complete to make a multiple of 9.

90

81

_7_

_6_

_5_

_4_

_3_

_2_

_1_

0 9

Count by 9s from 9 to 90:

_9_ ___ ___ ___ ___ ___ ___ ___ ___ _90_

Multiples of 9 (4)

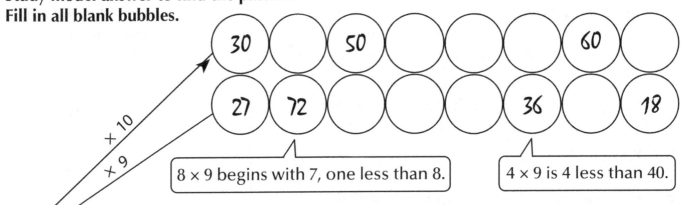

Study model answer to find the pattern.
Fill in all blank bubbles.

× 10
× 9
× 1

| 30 | | 50 | | | | 60 | |

| 27 | 72 | | | | 36 | | 18 |

8 × 9 begins with 7, one less than 8.

4 × 9 is 4 less than 40.

| 3 | 8 | | 7 | 9 | 4 | | |

9 × 6 begins with 1 less than 6.

Sum of the digits is 9.

9 × 6 begins with __5__ :   9 × 6 = __54__   __5__ + __4__ = __9__

9 × 2 begins with ____ :   9 × 2 = ____   ____ + ____ = ____

9 × 8 begins with ____ :   9 × 8 = ____   ____ + ____ = ____

9 × 4 begins with ____ :   9 × 4 = ____   ____ + ____ = ____

9 × 9 begins with ____ :   9 × 9 = ____ , 9 less than 90.

9 × 5 begins with ____ :   9 × 5 = ____ , 5 less than 50.

9 × 7 begins with ____ :   9 × 7 = ____ , 7 less than 70.

9 × 3 begins with ____ :   9 × 3 = ____ , 3 less than 30.

Write the unit digit to make multiples of 9 as in model:

5<u>4</u>   3<u> </u>   7<u> </u>   9<u> </u>   2<u> </u>   5<u> </u>   8<u> </u>   6<u> </u>

7<u> </u>   1<u> </u>   8<u> </u>   4<u> </u>   6<u> </u>   7<u> </u>   9<u> </u>   5<u> </u>

Multiples 9 (5)

$10 \times 7 = 7 + 7 + 7 + 7 + 7 + 7 + 7 + 7 + 7 + 7 = 70$

$9 \times 7 = 7 + 7 + 7 + 7 + 7 + 7 + 7 + 7 + 7 \cancel{(+ 7)} = 70 - 7 = $ _____

$9 \times 7 = 70 - 7 = 63.$ So: $63 + 7 = 70.$

Oral practice: Let students discover the pattern as above and acquire some fluency with oral practice before assigning the worksheet. Given a two-digit number that they recognize as a multiple of 9, they can use the pattern to know how many times 9 it is by answering the question: *"How much more to make 10 or a multiple of 10?"*
I give you a multiple of 9. How many times 9 is it?
        36?   4 times 9. (Think 4 more to make 10 or 40.)
        72?   8 times 9. 27? (3)   18? (2)   54? (6)   81? (9)   45? (5)   63? (7)

Multiples of 9: What is the second factor in the factor pair?

63: 3 + **7** = 10   9 (63) 7   18: 8 + **2** = 10   9 (18) 2

36: 6 + ___ = 10   9 (36)   81: 1 + ___ = 10   9 (81)

45: 5 + ___ = 10   9 (45)   27: 7 + ___ = 10   9 (27)

72: 2 + ___ = 10   9 (72)   54: 4 + ___ = 10   9 (54)

Use this pattern to find factor pairs for these multiples of 9:

9 (18) 2   9 (54)   9 (81)   (72)   (45)

(27)   (72)   (63)   (36)   (90)

(36)   (18)   (45)   (54)   (63)

Activity: Take 9 objects (tokens, cents, beans, etc.) They are "the sum of the digits."
Break them up to show tens and units of multiples of 9.

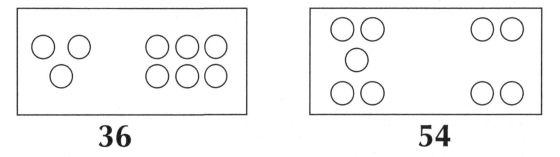

36   **54**

Break the 9 tokens up in order or at random. You or partner "read" the multiple of 9
shown by the tokens, "36," and give the math fact " 4 × 9," as in the model below.
Notice that "4" in "4 × 9" is one more than "3" in "36". Here, do this in writing:

With those 9 tokens on a page, if tokens show 36, turn the page upside down to show 63.

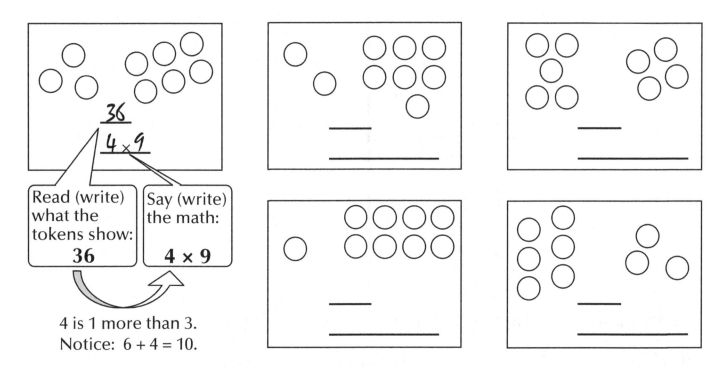

Read (write)
what the
tokens show:
36

Say (write)
the math:
4 × 9

4 is 1 more than 3.
Notice: 6 + 4 = 10.

Students, alone or in pairs, are expected to manipulate these 9 tokens freely, to break them up, read the
number that the partition represents, recognize that number as a multiple of 9, give the corresponding
"9 times" fact, and turn the sheet upside down to do the same with the new perspective.

A similar manipulation can be done with the fingers of both hands, but doing so has the disadvantage of
bypassing the mind, so to speak, and becoming for some students a complete substitute to leaning the
facts. Learning math facts has little to do with just having those facts available at all times – the calculator
on all phones does that quite well. The knowledge, on the other hand, opens the door to thinking in
terms of numbers and acquiring numeracy.

---

9 x 7 = 63   So 9 and 7 are a **factor pair** of 63.   9 —(63)— 7

Complete to show the other factor in the pair, as shown above.

| 1 more than 6. | or | What do I add to 3 to get 10? |

9 —(63)—   9 —(45)—   9 —(27)—   9 —(18)—   9 —(72)—

9 —(36)—   9 —(81)—   9 —(54)—   9 —(63)—   9 —(36)—

—(18)— 9   —(45)— 9   —(72)— 9   —(90)— 9   —(27)— 9

—(54)— 9   —(36)— 9   —(63)— 9   —(81)— 9   —(18)— 9

Think: 1 less than 8 to get the 7 of 72.

8 x 9 = _____   5 x 9 = _____

3 x 9 = _____   7 x 9 = _____

6 x 9 = _____   9 x 9 = _____

Think: 1 less than 4 to get the 3 of 36.

9 x 4 = _____   9 x 8 = _____

9 x 9 = _____   9 x 6 = _____

9 x 2 = _____   9 x 7 = _____

---

6 x 9 = ?   Think 1 less than 6 to get the 5 of 54.
72 = 9 x ?.   Think 1 more than 7 to get the 8 of 8 x 9.

"1 more"… "1 less": what if student doesn't remember which one to apply? Instead of reminding the student of the fact, teach the very powerful strategy of thinking of a simpler fact or another known fact:

Student: "72: is the factor of nine 1 more or 1 less than 7?"
You: "18: How many times 9?" or
            "What other 9-times fact do you know?"
            "So, is it 1 more or 1 less?"
            "What strategy did you use?"

The mental strategy of working something out with simpler or known numbers and then transferring the rule or pattern to the numbers at hand can be applied widely throughout a student's career and beyond. It needs to be experienced and discussed in multiple circumstances.

Guided practice. Oral review.

Thorough knowledge of 9 times fact family from 2 × 9 to 9 × 9 is essential. Let's return to three approaches that can be practiced orally in a few minutes as often as needed until the facts they represent become very familiar. They can be used much later as needed to review 9 times facts.

To recognize multiples of 9:

> I say "Twenty…?" You complete the number to make a multiple of 9:

| Twenty…? | "… seven. Twenty-seven."

| Fifty…? | "…four. Fifty- four."   "80…?"   "30…?"   "60…?"   "40…?"   "70…?"   "20…?"

The order in which the prompts are presented can help students review patterns:
      54/45.   27/72.   63/36.   18/81.
Or just: 18, 27, 36, 45, 54, 63, 72, 81, or vice versa.

To know the product when one factor is 9:

> I say "9 × 7?" (or "7 × 9?") You think of 1 less than 7 and immediately say: "Sixty…"
> Then you take your time if needed to complete the number: "…three. 9 × 7 is 63."

| 9 × 3? | "Twenty…seven. 9 × 3 is 27."   "9 × 8?"   "9 × 5?"   "9 × 7?"   "9 × 4?"   "9 × 9?"

To know the second factor of a 2-digit multiple of 9: Two strategies.

> I give you a multiple of 9: "72".
> You focus on the 2 of 72 and think: "2? How much more to make 10? 2 + 8 = 10,"
> and you say: "8 times 9. 72 is 8 times 9."

"27?"   "3. 27 is 3 times 9."   "45?"   "81?"   "18?"   "63?"   "90?"   "54?"   "36?"

> Or you can focus on the 7 of 72 and think: "One more than 7."
> So you say: "72 is 8 times 9."

Factor Pairs

Multiples of 2, 5, 9, 10

Write a Factor Pair of each number. Use factors from 2 to 10 only.

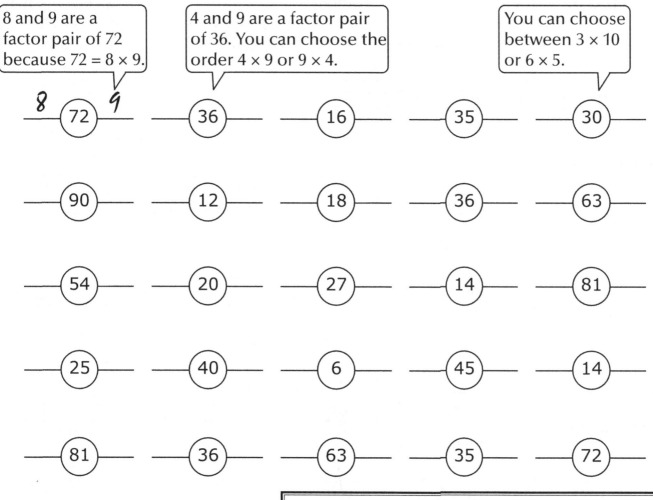

8 and 9 are a factor pair of 72 because 72 = 8 × 9.

4 and 9 are a factor pair of 36. You can choose the order 4 × 9 or 9 × 4.

You can choose between 3 × 10 or 6 × 5.

8   72   9

36   16   35   30

90   12   18   36   63

54   20   27   14   81

25   40   6   45   14

81   36   63   35   72

27   18

54   72

45   63

Students have just extensively practiced 9 times facts. This is the right time to begin conveying that knowledge to oral memory with the help of a vertical line from 1 to 10. They can initially do this while thinking of one of the mental strategies: 7 × 9 begins with 6, one less than 7. With this pattern in mind, as students say *aloud* "*7 × 9…*", they immediately think of 6 and say "*sixty…*". They conclude with the appropriate unit digit: "*…three.*"

From 2 × 2 to 9 × 9 there are 36 essential facts with single-digit factors. The "2-times", "5-times", and "9-times" facts studied in Level 1 represent 21 of these 36 facts, leaving only 15 new facts to master. Students will feel encouraged to know how much learning has already been achieved and how few essential facts still remain. Learning is discouraged when students face a challenge that they think overwhelming.

At any time, to review understanding and knowledge, students can be asked to speak freely about a number or an expression. Prompts by parents/teachers can ask them to explain, illustrate, or expand on their answers by giving other examples of the pattern or rule that the student is referring to. Prompts will adjust to students' answers and may be less needed as students become familiar with the process. In this sample **Number Talk,** we include statements that students will be able to make only later in our study.

Say all you can think of about this number:

Students may say:

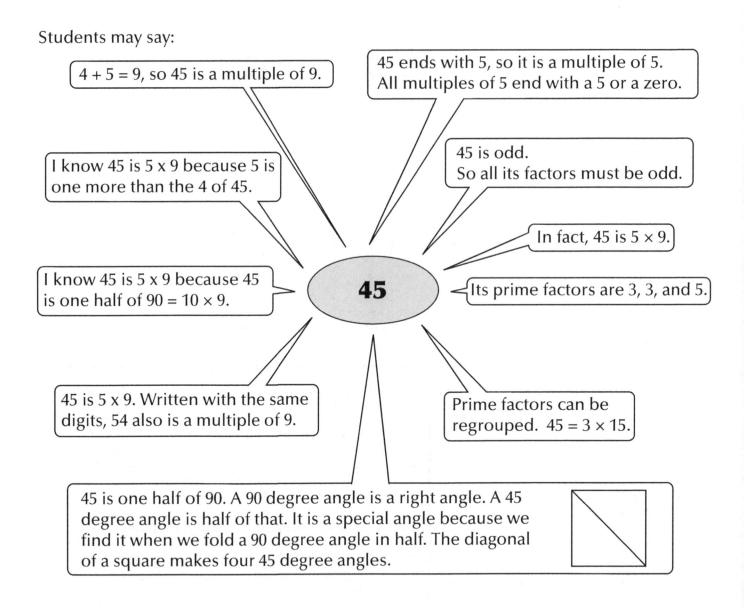

4 + 5 = 9, so 45 is a multiple of 9.

45 ends with 5, so it is a multiple of 5. All multiples of 5 end with a 5 or a zero.

I know 45 is 5 x 9 because 5 is one more than the 4 of 45.

45 is odd. So all its factors must be odd.

I know 45 is 5 x 9 because 45 is one half of 90 = 10 × 9.

In fact, 45 is 5 × 9.

Its prime factors are 3, 3, and 5.

45 is 5 x 9. Written with the same digits, 54 also is a multiple of 9.

Prime factors can be regrouped. 45 = 3 × 15.

45

45 is one half of 90. A 90 degree angle is a right angle. A 45 degree angle is half of that. It is a special angle because we find it when we fold a 90 degree angle in half. The diagonal of a square makes four 45 degree angles.

Knowledge itself is a thinking activity. We want students to review, not just the facts, but also the thinking strategies that can help them remember. **Number Talk** moments are a constantly available opportunity for doing so. Here, a very general question lets students take the initiative. If needed, additional prompts probe for more options. We suggest just the outline of prompts and of answers, more as an illustration than as the complete version of what can be expected.

> What helps you remember 9 times facts?

- Sum of the digits is 9. So I know that 18, 27, 36, 45 are multiples of 9.
- The sum is still 9 if I switch the digits. So 81, 72, 63, 54 are also multiples of 9.
- Students recognize 63 as a multiple of 9. The 7 of 7×9 is one more than the 6 of 63. 7 is also what you add to the 3 of 63 to get 10. Of these two strategies to identify the second factor, which do you prefer? Try them on 36? 81? 27? 54?

> What helps you multiply by 5?

- 5 is one half of 10. I can multiply by 10 and divide by 2. 5×7? I think $70 \div 2 = 35$.
- With even number 6, I can divide by 2 then multiply by 10: $6 \times 5 = 3 \times 10 = 30$.
- This approach lets me multiply larger numbers by 5: 5×16? I think of 8 to get 80.
- Multiples of 5 end with 5 or 0. All numbers that end with 5 or 0 are multiples of 5.
- 5 times an odd number ends with 5. 5 times an even number ends with 0.

> Tell me about double/half pairs.

- If all digits are even, I halve a number by dividing each digit by 2. $682 \div 2 = 341$.
- If all the digits are smaller than 5, I double the number by doubling each digit.
- Double/half pairs help me know multiples of 5 because I can multiply by 2 and divide by 10.

Flash cards

The approach used in *Making Friends with Numbers* is the opposite of the "drill and kill" approach generally associates with flash cards. But now that students have established connections and thinking strategies for knowing 2-times, 5-times and 9-times fact families, we can select the cards for these 21 facts. Flashed at random students can:
- Given the factors, give the product.
- Given the product, give the factor pairs.
- Discuss the mental strategies associated with any one of them. (See Number Talk.)
- Practice automaticity at a leisurely pace that can increase over time – without ever becoming a sprint to the finish that would preclude any possibility of some thinking activity coming to the rescue of uncertain knowledge.

Common Factor & Factor Pairs (1)

Multiples of 2, 5, 9, 10

Step 1:
Identify the common factor.

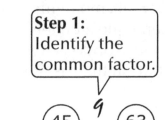

Step 2:
Show factor pairs of 45 and 63:
5 × 9 and 9 × 7.

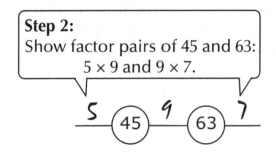

Show common factor and factor pairs as in model.
Use only factors from 2 to 10.

What factor do 27 and 15 have in common?

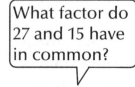

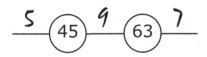

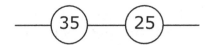

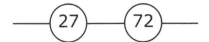

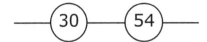

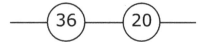

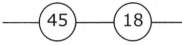

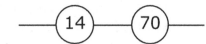

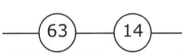

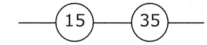

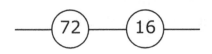

Practice makes perfect.
But practice makes sense only if it applies to what is already essentially known and understood. Here, as with most of the practice sheets that follow, parents/teachers can make sure that students are ready for the practice material by having students read, explain, discuss, and illustrate orally or on scratch paper the pattern or material to be practiced. Beyond assigning a worksheet, teachers/parents can make sure that students understand the initial model and transfer its pattern correctly orally or in writing to the first examples that follow.

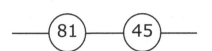

Common Factor & Factor Pairs (2)   1-31

Show common factor and factor pairs as in model.
Use only factors from 2 to 10.

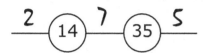

2 (14) 7 (35) 5

(25) — (15)

(18) — (72)

(54) — (12)

(14) — (63)

(36) — (27)

(80) — (30)

(35) — (45)

(72) — (81)

(45) — (18)

(16) — (72)

(54) — (45)

(63) — (14)

(81) — (18)

(27) — (72)

Looking ahead

Finding the Common Factor between two numbers is an essential skill, with multiple applications. Students familiar with this approach to learning multiplication facts will have a considerable advantage when they begin to study fractions. Using the numbers in the first example on this page, 14 and 35, an ability to see common factor 7 is needed to simplify fraction 14/35 which becomes 2/5. Also, two fractions with denominators 14 and 35 can be added using common denominator $2 \times 7 \times 5 = 2 \times 35 = 70$. What students are learning here, and how they are learning essential facts, will serve them well. Initially, we are asking students to find a common factor 10 or smaller, not necessarily the Greatest Common Factor. That skill will be explored later in *Making Friends with Numbers*.

Improvised *Number Talk* sessions offer options for students to formulate the facts, thinking strategies and connections they have already studied. Along with the Oral/Rhythmic practice of fact families, some form of *Number Talk* could become a regular feature of most math sessions.

What follows represents two more approaches to reviewing and practicing what has already been seen:
• The *Factor Chains* are a playful way of practicing essential multiplication facts by finding common factors and factor pairs. They are almost self-correcting, as getting one factor wrong makes it difficult to find the following factor. In a few minutes student can review all the facts studied so far.
• The *Messed-up Times Squares* are also convenient options for practicing essential facts. Both *Factor Chains* and *Messed-up Times Squares* can be assigned at will by parents/teachers. They can be mixed up, alternatively one and then the other. If essentially mastered by students, some sheets can be left out or kept for future review.

Factor Chain

Multiples of 2, 5, 9, 10

Guided Discovery

Numbers in the chain are linked by a common factor.
These common factors also show a factor pair of each number.
Use only factors from 2 to 10.

As you begin, think of: ⁹—(45)—⁵—(10)—²—

Study and complete this factor chain.

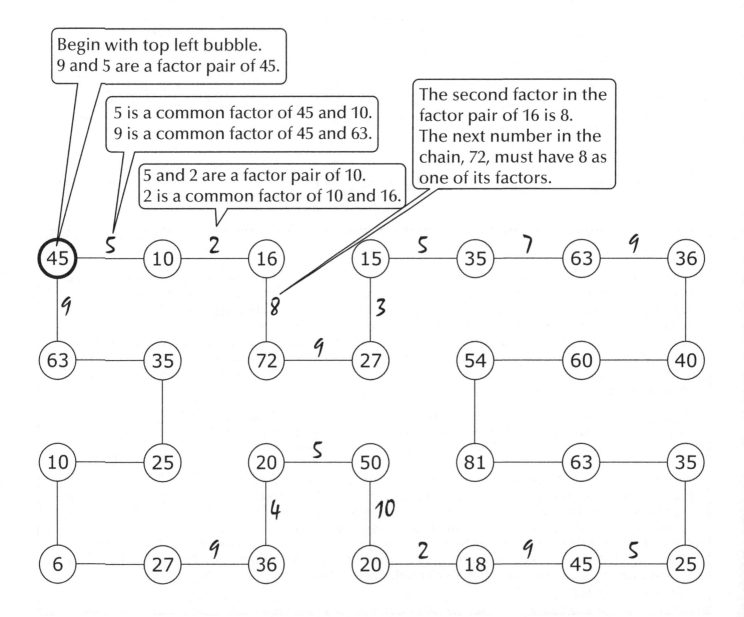

Begin with top left bubble.
9 and 5 are a factor pair of 45.

5 is a common factor of 45 and 10.
9 is a common factor of 45 and 63.

5 and 2 are a factor pair of 10.
2 is a common factor of 10 and 16.

The second factor in the factor pair of 16 is 8.
The next number in the chain, 72, must have 8 as one of its factors.

Factor Chain

Multiples of 2, 5, 9, 10.

As you move along the chain, write **common factors** and **factor pairs** as shown.
Begin with factor pair of top left bubble. Use only factors from 2 to 10.

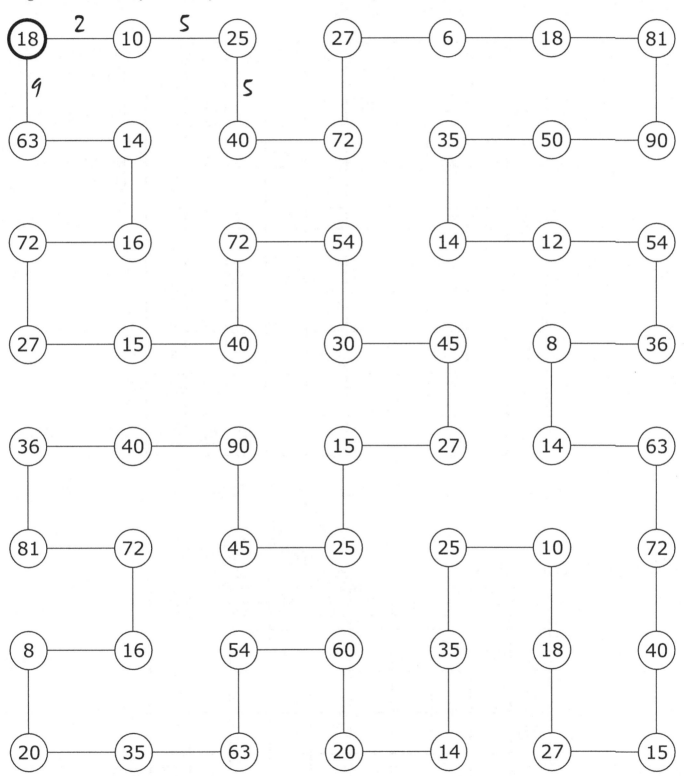

Multiples of 2, 5, 9, 10.

Guided Discovery

Fill in columns and rows 2, 5, 9, 10, as modeled.
They show the 30 facts that you have practiced on Level 1.

The factors from 2 to 10.

Where row 5 and column 9 meet, write **45**, the product of the two factors.

×	2	3	4	5	6	7	8	9	10
2	4	6	8	10					
3	6								
4	8								
5								45	
6									
7									
8									80
9									90
10							80	90	100

Now, the order is messed up.

×	7	2	8	5	6	3	10	4	9
9	63	18							
5									
10									90
2								8	18

Guided Discovery

The factors are not in order, and it's not a square.

Fill in all the blank cells with multiples of 2, 5, 9, and 10.
Fill in shaded cells with factors from 2 to 10 in top row, factors 2, 5, 9 and 10 on the left.

> **Clue:** You know the two factors that rule this cell (10 and 4). Write in the product (40).

> **Clue:** Perfect square 25 has only 5 as a factor, twice. Write in those two factors in the gray cells for the column and the row.

> **Clue:** 40, 25, and 30 have 5 as a common factor. Write 5 in the shaded cell for the row. The three columns must be 8, 5, and 6.

> **Clue:** 63 and 14 have only 7 as a common factor. 7 rules this column.

			4			9			3
10							20		
		40		25				30	
	63								
	14				20				

> Don't let all these numbers spook you. Take it one step at time. Look for a clue. Solve it. Move on.

> Like a crossword puzzle it doesn't make much difference where you begin and the cells that you solve help you solve other cells.

Try it here:

> In these shaded cells: The nine factors from 2 to 10, not in order.

> In these shaded cells: Factors 2, 5, 9, 10, not in order.

			4			9			3
10							20		
		40		25				30	
	63								
	14				20				

Messed-Up Times Squares & Rectangles 1-36

Fill in all the cells.

Assign just one puzzle at a time, not all three.

Multiples of 2, 5, 9, 10.

1-38 (1)

In horizontal grey cells: Factors from 2 to 10.

In vertical grey cells: Factors 2, 5, 9, 10.

		7					4		8
	30				50			60	
		63				90			
			45						
			18	4					

1-38 (2)

						5			
9	18			90					
			15		30			40	
		90					70		40
2									

1-38 (3)

			3			5	
10							60
		36	81				
	35				50		
				16	4		

Factor Chain

Multiples of 2, 5, 9, 10.

Show **common factors** and **factor pairs**.
Use only factors from 2 to 10.

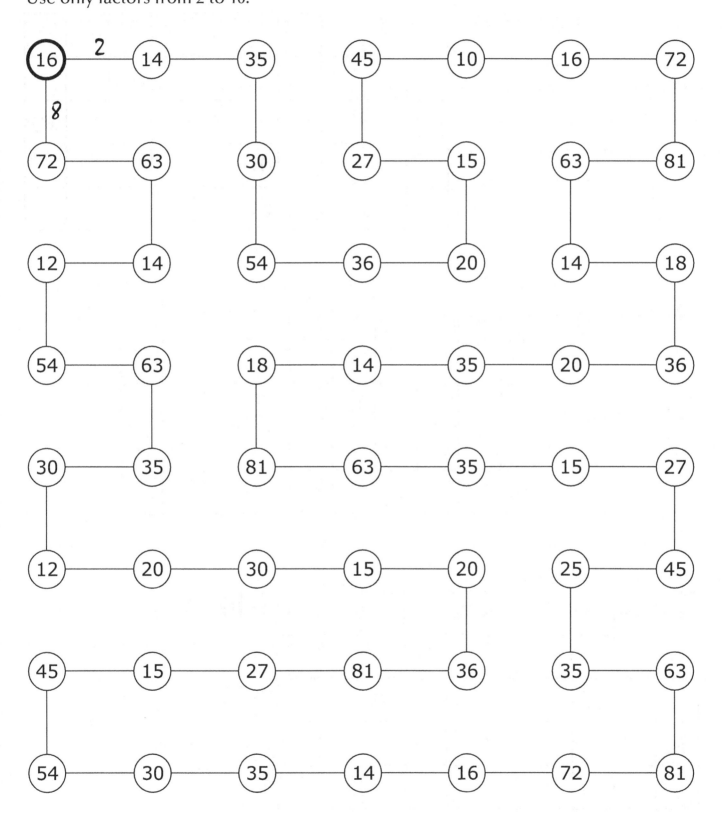

Fill in all the cells. Multiples of 2, 5, 9, 10.

1-40 (1)

In horizontal grey cells: Put factors from 2 to 10.

In vertical grey cells: Put factors 2, 5, 9, 10.

	6		10			3			
		36					63		
				4					10
			40					45	
			80						

1-40 (2)

	4					3		
	70							
			18	72				
	14						10	18
5		50		30				

1-40 (3)

	9			8			4
5				15			
		20			14		
10							
			45	18			54

Factor Chain

Multiples of 2, 5, 9, 10.

Show **common factors** and **factor pairs.**
Use only factors from 2 to 10.

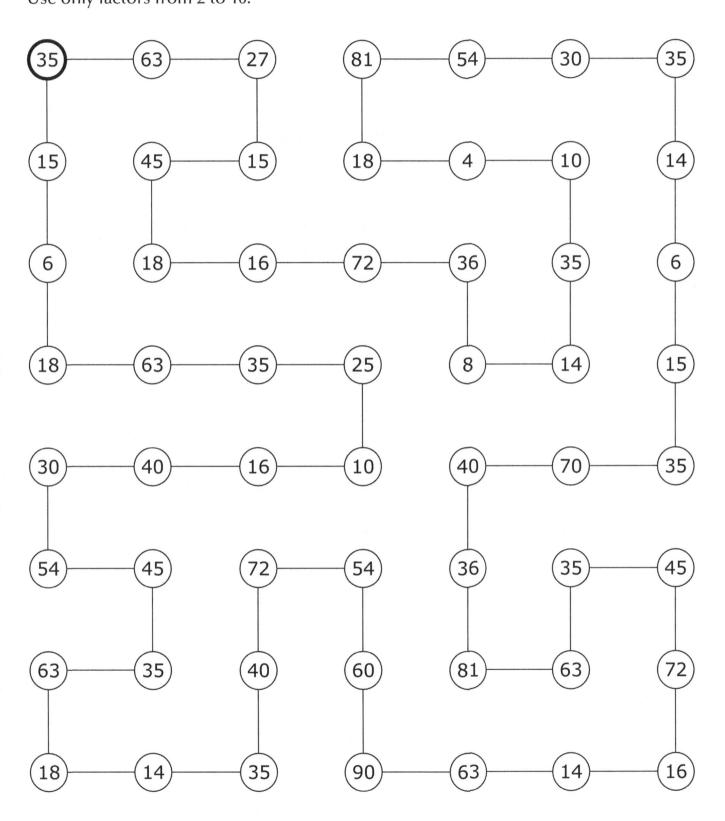

Factor Chain

Show **common factors** and **factor pairs**.
Use single digit factors.

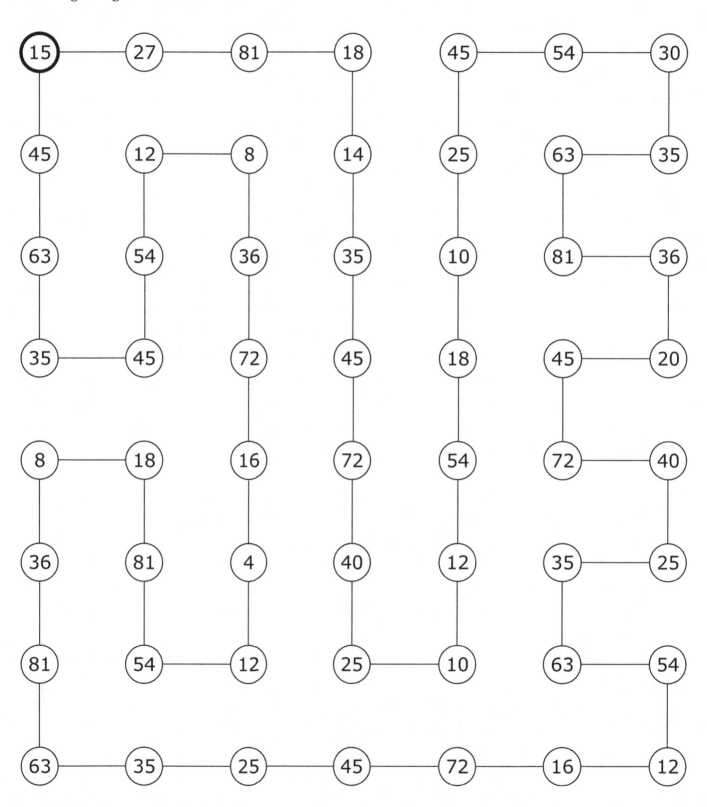

Factor Chain

Show **common factors** and **factor pairs.**
Use only factors from 2 to 9.

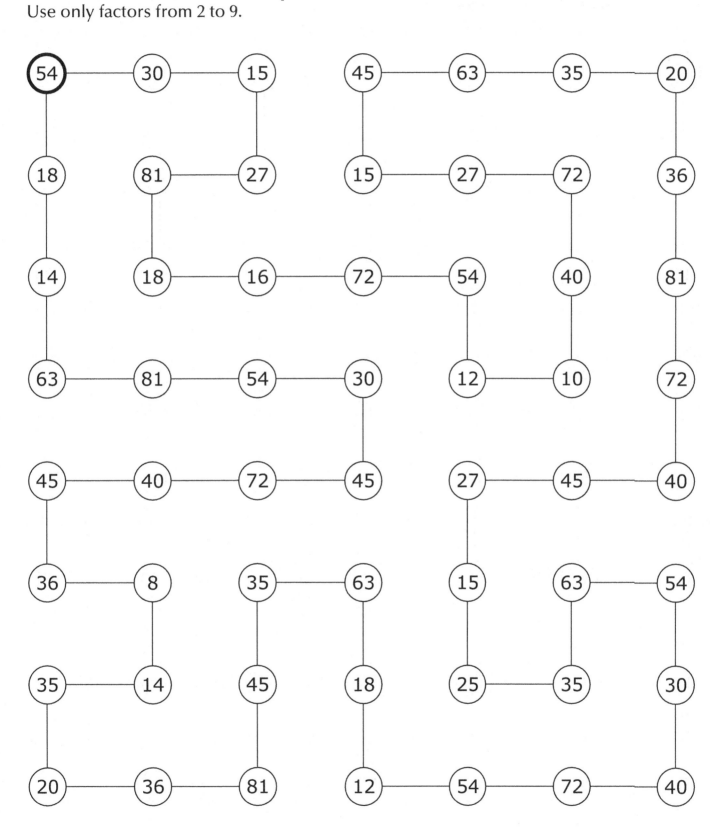

Factor Chain

Multiples of 2, 5, 9.

Show **common factors** and **factor pairs.**

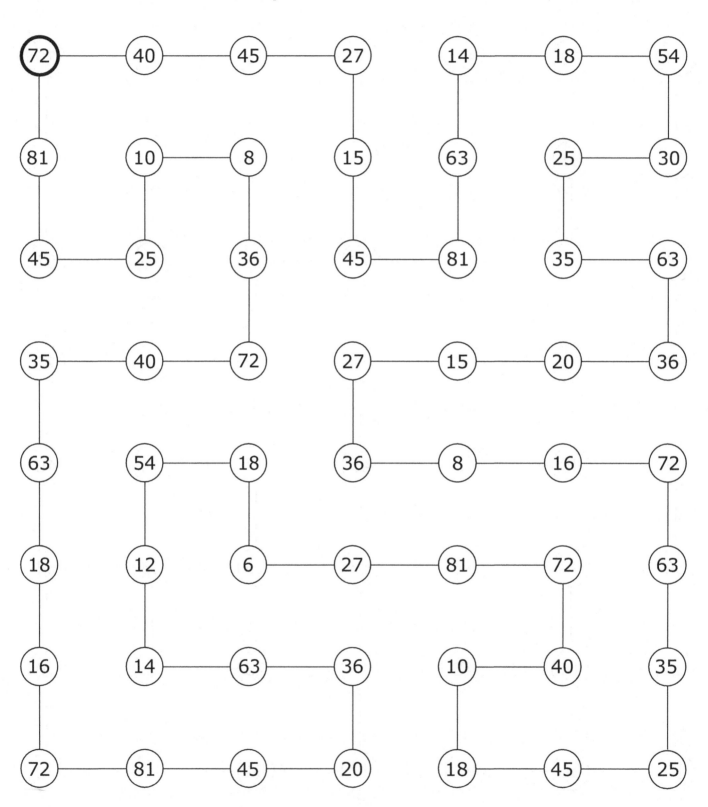

Let's first become familiar with 8 new facts.

We add five square numbers that we have not yet seen: ⎯⎯⎯

$3 \times 3 =$ _____

$4 \times 4 =$ _____

$6 \times 6 =$ _____

$7 \times 7 =$ _____

$8 \times 8 =$ _____

We also add:

$3 \times 4 =$ _____

$3 \times 7 =$ _____

$7 \times 8 =$ _____

SQUARE NUMBERS

Square numbers are the product of **two equal factors.**
They can be written using the factor and the **exponent** 2.

64 is a "square" because $64 = 8 \times 8$.

The factor 8... ...is used twice.

$$64 = 8^2 = 8 \times 8$$

Circle these eight new facts:

1	2	3	4	5	6	7	8	9
2	4							
3	6	9						
4	8	12	16					
5	10	15	20	25				
6	12	18	24	30	36			
7	14	21	28	35	42	49		
8	16	24	32	40	48	56	64	
9	18	27	36	45	54	63	72	81

We have already studied the facts in the shaded cells.

Fill in: ⎯(12)⎯(21)⎯(56)⎯

Students learn best when they feel confident that what they are asked to achieve is achievable. As they begin Level 2, a conversation with parent/teacher about what has already been done in Level 1 and what remains to be learned makes a lot of sense:

- *Our first priority is to know multiplications facts with single-digit factors, from 2 × 2 to 9 × 9.*
- *How many facts is that?* (Let students find answer. The Times Square table might help.)
- *Why are these facts so important?* (If we know them, we can calculate all other facts.)
- *Which fact families have we already studied?* (2 times, 5 times, 9 times facts.)
- *With single-digit factors, how many facts is that?*
- *So we need to learn 36 facts and we are already familiar with 21. How many more do we need to learn? Only 15!*

With feet (marching?) or fist keeping the rhythm, repeat with a slow steady beat:

1   2   3   4   5   6   7   8

On the same 4-beat rhythm, marking the rhythm with feet or fist, repeat as needed:

Read with even beat: Read with even beat:

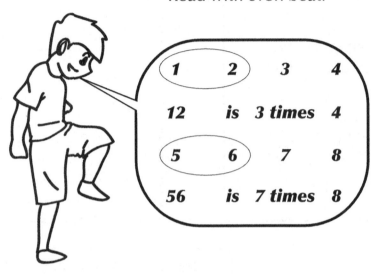

1	2	3	4
12	is	3 times	4
5	6	7	8
fifty -	six is	7 times	8

Based on that information:

12 = _____ × _____   You see 12, and you keep counting: 3 times 4.

56 = _____ × _____   You see 56 and you keep counting: 7 times 8.

Link numbers with common factors and factor pairs. Focus on Squares in ☐, 12, 21, 56.

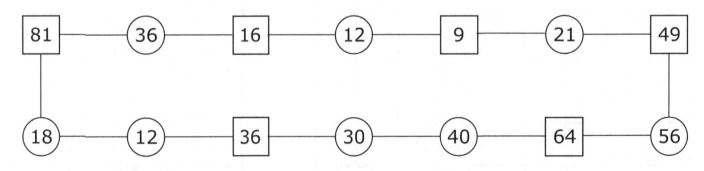

Before assigning this page, have students march as shown. Also discuss with them:
• Tell me about the Sum of the Digits for multiples of 9. It helps you recognize multiples of 9.
• In the same way, the Sum of the Digits for multiples of 3 is 3 or a multiple of 3 (3, 6, 9, etc.)
• Find examples of multiples of 3. How can you tell they are multiples of 3?
• 1 + 2 = 3. So give me two numbers easy to recognize as multiples of 3. (12 = 3 × 4 and 21 = 3 × 7)

Square Numbers (1)

The first square numbers are: 4, 9, 16, 25, 36, 49, 64, 81, 100.

Write these square numbers using the exponent 2:

9 = 3^2 64 = _____   16 = _____

81 = _____   36 = _____   4 = _____

25 = _____   100 = _____   49 = _____

Vocabulary: 64 is the **square** of 8.   8 is the **square root** of 64.

The **square root** of 49 is _____.   The **square root** of 81 is _____.

The **square root** of 64 is _____.   The **square root** of 36 is _____.

5 is the _____ of 25.   4 is the _____ of 16.

The square of an even number has 2 as a factor. It is _____.

$2 \times 2 =$ _____ $4 \times 4 =$ _____ $6 \times 6 =$ _____ $8 \times 8 =$ _____

The square of an odd number is _____.   (Even / Odd)

$3 \times 3 =$ _____ $5 \times 5 =$ _____ $7 \times 7 =$ _____ $9 \times 9 =$ _____

Show factors pairs. Use the **square root** as factors for square numbers.

 ⎯(64)⎯   ⎯(81)⎯   ⎯(49)⎯   ⎯(4)

⎯(25)⎯   ⎯(9)⎯   ⎯(100)⎯   ⎯(36)

"5, 6, 7, 8; 56 is 7 × 8."

 ⎯(56)⎯   ⎯(21)⎯   ⎯(63)⎯   ⎯(64)

Square Numbers (2)

The first square numbers are:

4							81
2 × 2	3 × 3	4 × 4	5 × 5	6 × 6	7 × 7	8 × 8	9 × 9

Fill in factor pairs to show two different factor pairs for 12, 16, and 36:

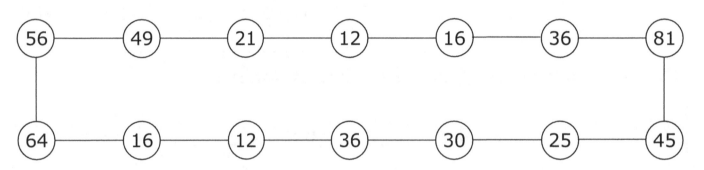

Link with common factors and factor pairs.
Focus on square numbers and 12, 21, 56.

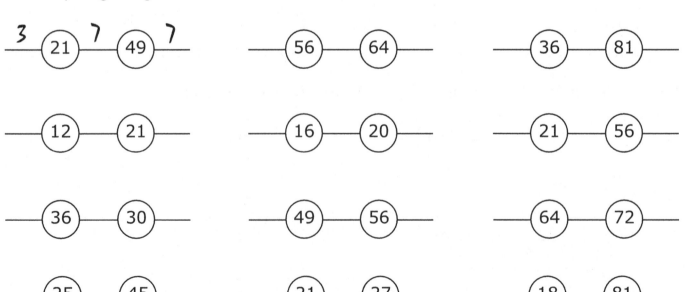

Show common factor and factor pairs as in model.
Use only single-digit factors.

Area

Best presented by parent/teacher as a guided discovery.

How many happy faces?

_____ columns with _____ happy faces in each: 3 × 5 = _____ 15 happy faces.

_____ rows with _____ happy faces in each: 5 × 3 = _____ 15 happy faces.

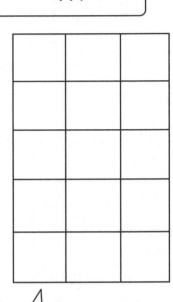

Each small square is a **square unit**
used to measure the area of the rectangle.

How many **square units** are there in the larger rectangle?

_____ columns with _____ **square units** in each: 3 × 5 = _____ 15 **square units.**

_____ rows with _____ **square units** in each: 5 × 3 = _____ 15 **square units.**

If a rectangle (as above) measures 3 feet by 5 feet, it has:
    3 columns with 5 square feet in each column or
    5 rows with 3 square feet in each row
for a total area of 15 square feet.

The math: _____ square units.

Area of Squares

$3 \times 3 = 3^2 = 9$ $4 \times 4 = 4^2 = 16$ $6 \times 6 = 6^2 = 36$ $7 \times 7 = 7^2 = 49$ $8 \times 8 = 8^2 = 64$

Each small square is a **square unit** used to measure the area of the larger squares.
How many square units in each of these squares?

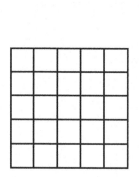

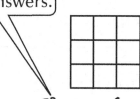

Use exponent 2 in your answers.

Area = ___3^2___ = ___9___ square units.

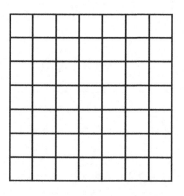

Area = _____ = _____ square units.

Area = _____ = _____ square units.

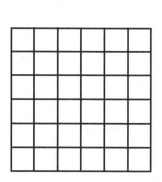

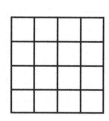

Area = _____ = _____ square units.

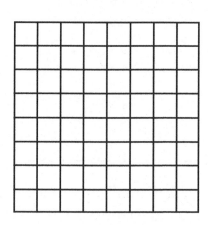

Area = _____ = _____ square units.

Area = _____ = _____ square units.

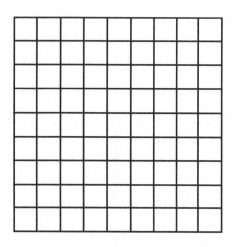

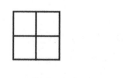

Area = _____ = _____ square units.

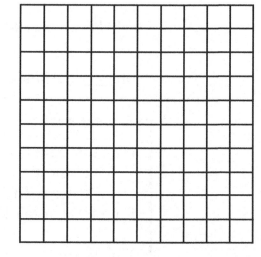

Area = _____ = _____ square units.

Area = _____ = _____ square units.

Area of Rectangles

Not to scale

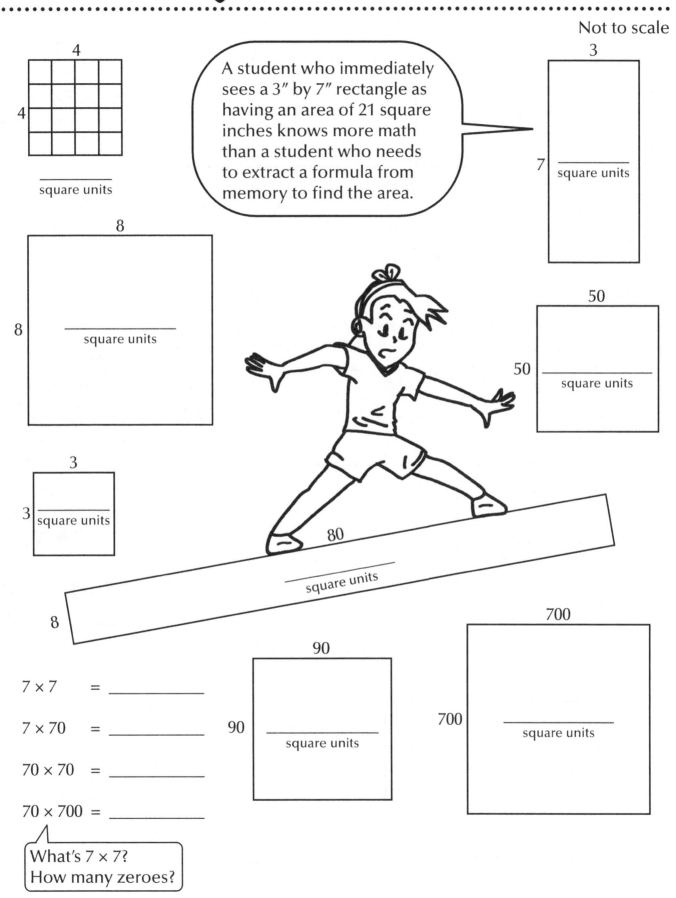

4

4

_____
square units

A student who immediately sees a 3″ by 7″ rectangle as having an area of 21 square inches knows more math than a student who needs to extract a formula from memory to find the area.

3

7 _____
square units

8

8 _____
square units

50

50 _____
square units

3

3 _____
square units

80

_____
square units

8

90

90 _____
square units

700

700 _____
square units

7 × 7   = _____

7 × 70   = _____

70 × 70 = _____

70 × 700 = _____

What's 7 × 7?
How many zeroes?

© Edric Cane 2020   Copying without written permission is illegal.

49

Area of Rectangles

Not to scale

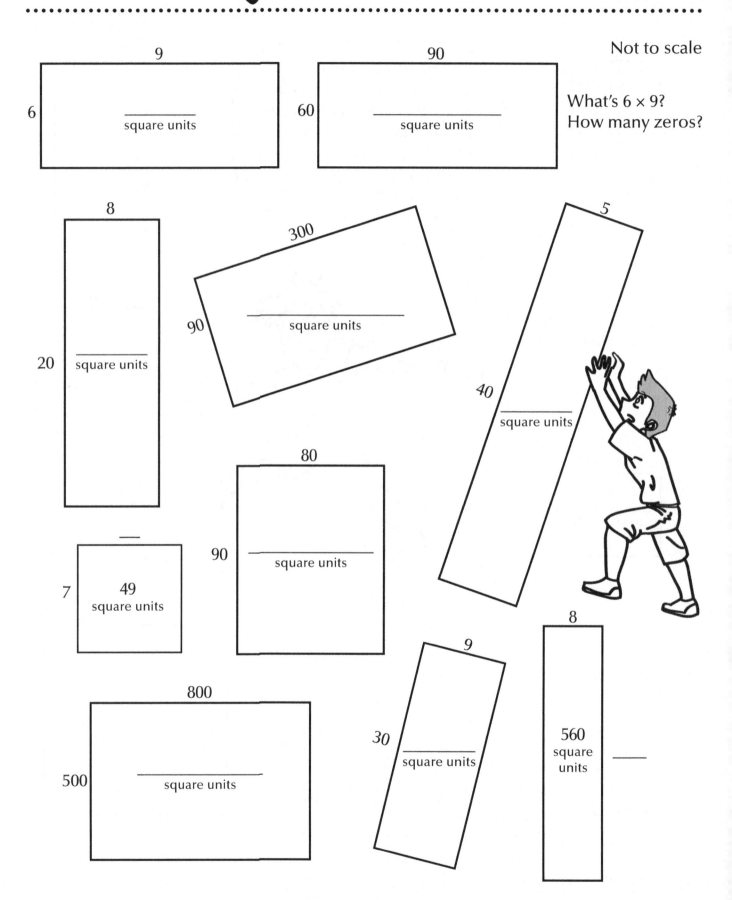

9

6
_____
square units

90

60
_____
square units

What's 6 × 9?
How many zeros?

8

20
_____
square units

300

90
_____
square units

5

40
_____
square units

80

90
_____
square units

___

7
49
square units

800

500
_____
square units

9

30
_____
square units

8

560
square
units
___

Area of Rectangles

Not to scale

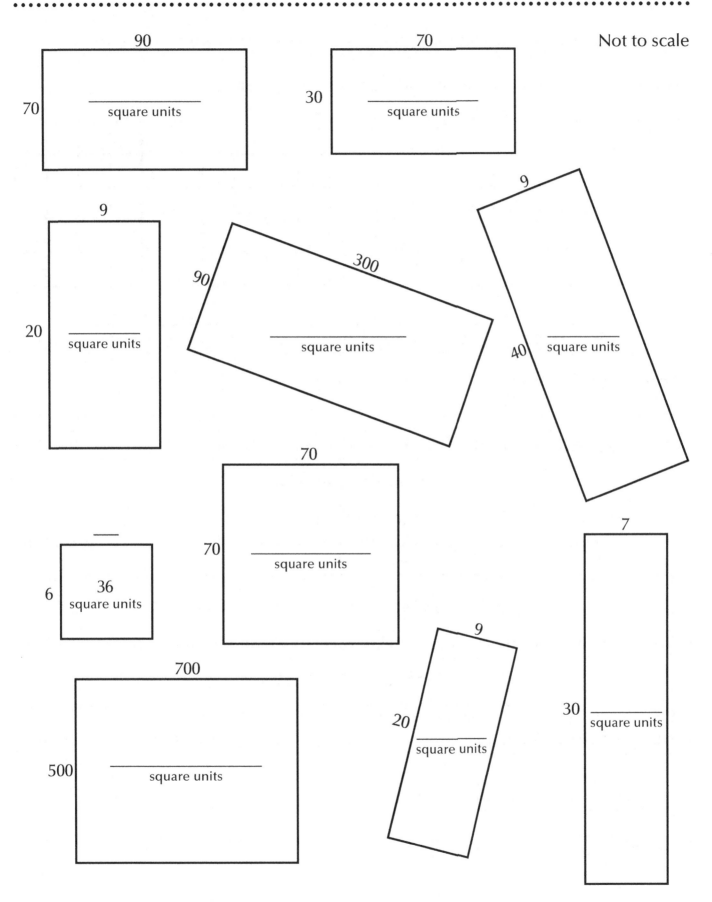

90

70 _____ square units

70

30 _____ square units

9

20 _____ square units

90 300 _____ square units

9

40 _____ square units

70

70 _____ square units

___

6   36 square units

7

30 _____ square units

9

20 _____ square units

700

500 _____ square units

Squares and Neighbors (1)

Guided Discovery. Connections between squares and neighboring numbers.

Students draw a 4 by 4 square (on grid paper with large cells?)

| What is the area? | $4 \times 4 = 16$ |

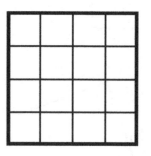 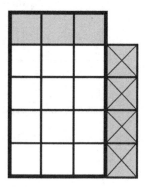

| Cross out a column on one side. How many cells did you cross out? | 4 |

| Add a row on top or on the bottom. How many cells did you add? | 3 |

| You take away 4 cells and you add 3. So what is the area of the new rectangle? | 15 |

| What are its dimensions? | $15 = 3 \times 5$ |

| The height is 5, 1 more than 4; The width is 3, 1 less than 4. The area is 15, 1 less than 16. |

| Let's try that with a 7×7 square. What's the area? | $7 \times 7 = 49.$ |
| What rectangle do you get by crossing out a column and adding a row? | $6 \times 8 = 48.$ |
| So what's the connection between 49 and 48? |

49 is the square of 7. You get 48 by multiplying 1 less than 7 by 1 more than 7.

| Check with other square numbers you know. | *25/24   64/63   36/35   9/8   49/48.* |

| Write three consecutive numbers such as 23, 24, 25. What can you say about them? | *24 × 24 is one more than 23 × 25.* |

| $13^2 = 169$. What is 12 x 14? | *168* |

| $15^2 = 225$. What is 14 x 16? | *224* |

Squares and Neighbors (2)

Study the model. Use the single clue to fill in one more cell. Then another. Then another.

Fill in multiples and factor pairs to illustrate that, if we take three consecutive numbers such as 7, 8, 9, the square of the middle number ($8 \times 8 = 64$) is 1 more than the product of the two extremes ($7 \times 9 = 63$). **Here, square numbers are written in square cells.**

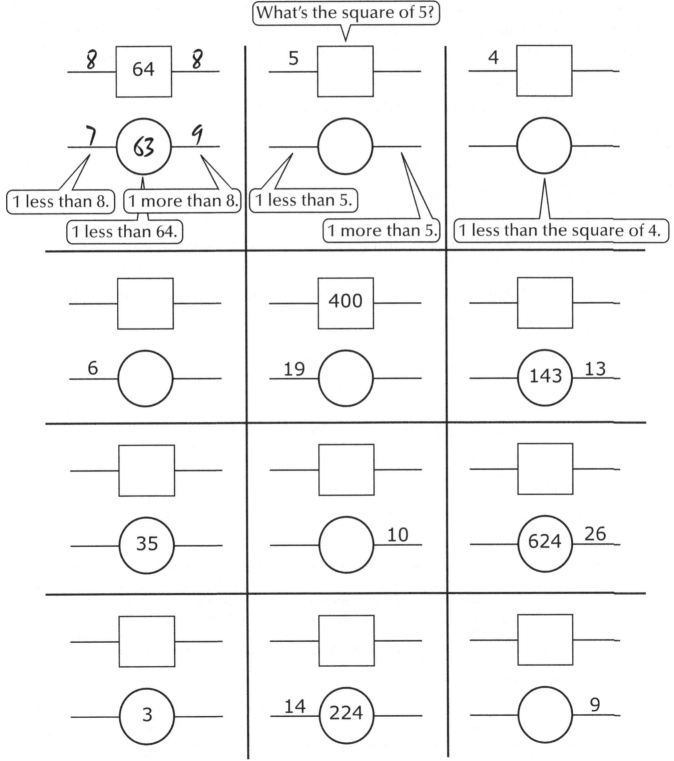

Guided Discovery Presented by parent/teacher in a conversation with students.

The aim is to help students discover a very obvious observation and encourage them to use their imagination to put it to good use.

One of these answers is correct. Which one?

(Students will make guesses, give their reasons. Some may even get it right for the right reason.)

> $473 \times 837 =$ a) 392,643
> b) 395,901
> c) 396,789

What are the unit digits of factors 473 and 837?

3 and 7.

What's 3×7?

$3 \times 7 = 21$.

What's the unit digit of that product?

The 1 of 21.

Which option – a, b, c – has 1 as its unit digit?

b) 395,901.

So how can you tell that options a) and c) are wrong?

The correct answer must have 1 as its unit digit.

Do you think this applies to all multiplications?

Yes.

Let's see how that can help with these numbers.

> **84   96**

Let's imagine you know that 84 and 96 are multiples of 12. (They are.) How can you tell which one is 8×12?

It's 96.
8×2 is 16. So 8×12 must also have 6 as its unit digit.

Here, we know what we want students to observe. This does not mean that we – or the students – have to formulate that knowledge in general terms, in words that apply to all circumstances. (This would be mathematical legalese: "The unit digit of the product of two numbers is always the same as the unit digit of the product of the unit digits of the two numbers.") Students would find it confusing to keep track of which unit digit we are referring to at any one point. We use a practical example which we allow students to generalize to all multiplications. Mathematical knowledge is not embodied in confusing definitions or formulations, however accurate they may be.

When students learn the formal algorithm for multiplication (each parent/teacher decides when and how this should be done), then they can see how obvious this observation on the unit digits really is.

Odd × Odd = Odd

Guided Discovery

"The factors of my factors are my factors."

$$9 \quad \times \quad 10 \quad = \quad 90$$
$$\downarrow \qquad\qquad \downarrow \qquad\qquad \downarrow$$
$$3 \times 3 \quad \times \quad 2 \times 5 \quad = \quad 3 \times 3 \times 2 \times 5$$

> Numbers have all the factors of their factors. 10 has 2 as a factor. It is even. So 90 also has 2 as a factor and is even.

> A product is even when **any one of its factors** is even.
>
> A product is odd only **if all its factors** are odd.

ODD × ODD = ODD

> Where would 2, the even factor, come from?

There are more even multiples than odd ones in our Times Square.

In this Times Square:

Number of EVEN multiples:
(Shaded cells from 4 to 72.)

———————

Number of ODD multiples:
(In white cells from 9 to 81.)

———————

Below, show the ten ODD multiples and their factor pairs:

1	2	3	4	5	6	7	8	9
2	4							
3	6	9						
4	8	12	16					
5	10	15	20	25				
6	12	18	24	30	36			
7	14	21	28	35	42	49		
8	16	24	32	40	48	56	64	
9	18	27	36	45	54	63	72	81

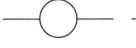
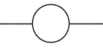
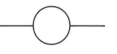

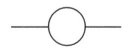
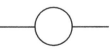
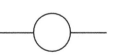

Odd × Odd Factor Chain

Show **common factors** and **factor pairs. Use only odd factors 3, 5, 7, 9.**
There are only 10 odd multiples that keep coming back and back.

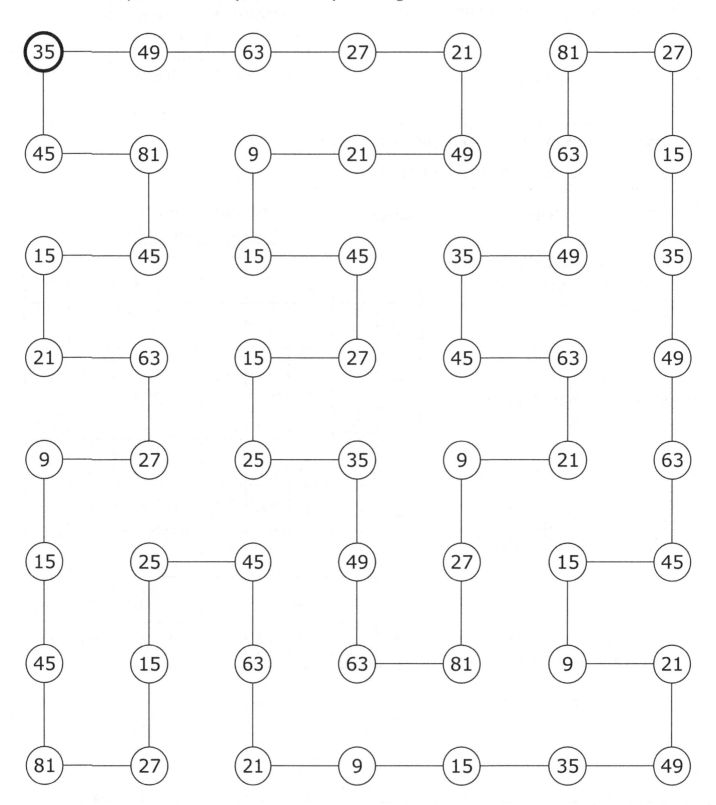

Odd × Odd Factor Chain

Show **common factors** and **factor pairs. Use only odd factors 3, 5, 7, 9.**
There are only 10 odd multiples. Know them well.

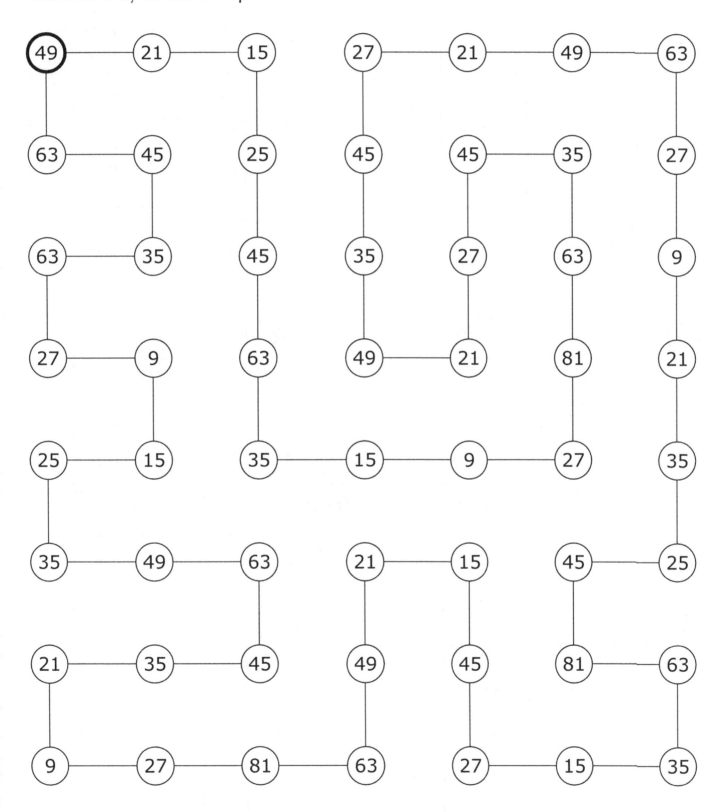

Messed-Up Times Squares

Use only odd factors 3, 5, 7, 9 (in shaded cells) and their odd multiples (in white cells) to fill in all the cells.

(1)

	3	5	7	9
3				
5				
7				
9				

(2)

	9	3	5	7
3				
9				
7				
5				

(3)

				9
	35		15	
		35		
			27	
		15		

(4)

	7			
		27		9
				21
9			45	
5				

(5)

3				
				49
		45	25	
	27		45	

(6)

9				
		21		
	27		21	
		15		25

What factor do 27 and 21 have in common?

We now begin studying systematically each remaining fact family with single-digit factors: 7, 3, 6, 4, 8. Before assigning written practice, each family should be introduced orally. Students will:
- Discover how much they already know about that fact family.
- Review those known facts and the connections and mental strategies that help remember.
- Discover how few new facts remain to be learned in that family and discover the connections and mental strategies that can help. Doubling a known fact is a frequent connection.
- Review the whole fact family orally with the help of the vertical lines on the back cover.

Let's study the 7-times family. Write in a column numbers from 1 to 10.

$1 \times 7 = 7$

$2 \times 7 = 14$

$3 \times 7 = 21$

④

$5 \times 7 = 35$

⑥

$7 \times 7 = 49$

$8 \times 7 = 56$

$9 \times 7 = 63$

$10 \times 7 = 70$

- You know 1×7 and 10×7. Write them down.
- You know multiples of 2, 5, and 9. Write those down.
- What about 3 times 7? *(21)* Write it down.
- What's the square of 7? Write it down.
- "5, 6, 7, 8; 56 is ___?____"   Write 7×8 down.

| What do we still need to learn? | *4 times 7 and 6 times 7.*
|---|

- What's 2 times 7? *(14)* What's 14 + 14? *(28)* So what's 4 times 7? *(28)*
- What's 3 times 7? *(21)* What's 21 + 21? *(42)* So what's 6 times 7? *(42)*

If you forget, how can you remember that 28 and 42 are multiples of 7?

- When you see 28, can you immediately divide it by 2? Why?   (Even digits.)
  14 has 7 as a factor. So 2 times 14 also has 7 as a factor: $2 \times 2 \times 7 = 4 \times 7 = 28$.
- Can you immediately divide 42 by 2? Why?
  Does 21 have 7 as a factor? So does 42 also have 7 as a factor?
- If you're not quite sure about $4 \times 7 = 28$ or 6 times 7 = 42, think of 2×7 and 3×7.

Count by 7s from 7 to 70. Take your time.   What's 21 + 7?   What's 42 + 7?

Use the lines on the back cover to practice the 7-times fact family: *"1 times 7, 7; etc."* You may want to do it only to the square of 7: *"7 × 7 = 49."* See page 20.

Multiples of 7 (2)

Count by 7 from 7 to 84. Do it in writing and do it orally.

7
1×

___
2×

___
3×

___
4×

___
5×

___
6×

___
7×

___
8×

___
9×

___
10×

___
11×

84
12×

| $7 \times 7 = 7^2$. | "5, 6, 7, 8; _____ is 7 × 8." | Think 10 × 7 = 70 plus 2 × 7 = 14 or 2 × 42. |

Double a factor and double the product.

2 × 7 = ____ | 3 × 7 = ____ | 4 × 7 = ____ | 5 × 7 = ____

4 × 7 = ____ | 6 × 7 = ____ | 8 × 7 = ____ | 10 × 7 = ____

Add these numbers. Notice the pattern:

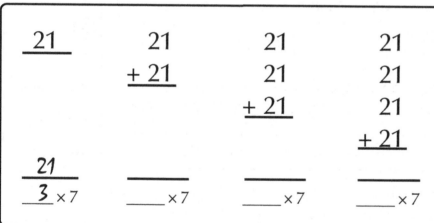

```
  21          21          21          21
_____        + 21         21          21
                        + 21          21
                                    + 21

  21         _____       _____       _____
 _3_ × 7     ____ × 7    ____ × 7    ____ × 7
```

This is not busy-work.

THINK about the connections.

LEARN from them.

Write in the factor pairs:

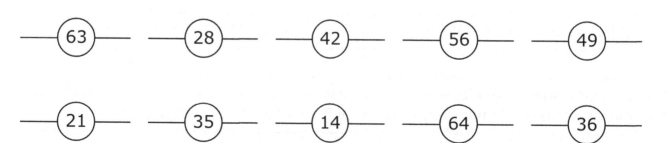

—(63)—   —(28)—   —(42)—   —(56)—   —(49)—

—(21)—   —(35)—   —(14)—   —(64)—   —(36)—

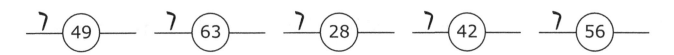

Write in the missing factor(s).

7 (49) ___   7 (63) ___   7 (28) ___   7 (42) ___   7 (56) ___

___ (35) ___   ___ (21) ___   ___ (14) ___   ___ (63) ___   ___ (49) ___

___ (28) ___   ___ (56) ___   ___ (35) ___   ___ (21) ___   ___ (42) ___

Show common factor and factor pairs as in model.
Use only factors from 2 to 10.

7 (21) 3 (15) 5 ___   ___ (56) ___ (49) ___   ___ (42) ___ (36) ___

___ (63) ___ (35) ___   ___ (14) ___ (16) ___   ___ (28) ___ (36) ___

___ (56) ___ (64) ___   ___ (21) ___ (9) ___   ___ (28) ___ (35) ___

___ (56) ___ (63) ___   ___ (16) ___ (56) ___   ___ (21) ___ (56) ___

___ (49) ___ (63) ___   ___ (42) ___ (56) ___

Add 7 times fact family to ORAL practice using a line from 1 to 10. Do it while facts are still present in memory.

Multiples of 3 (1)

Help students discover what they know and what they still need to learn. See Multiples of 7.

Count by 3s from 3 to 36 orally and in writing. Circle the facts you know.

$\underline{3}$	___	___	___	___	___	___	___	___	___	___	$\underline{36}$
1×	2×	3×	4×	5×	6×	7×	8×	9×	10×	11×	12×

Based on these numbers:

$4 \times 3 =$ _____ $12 \times 3 =$ _____ $8 \times 3 =$ _____ $5 \times 3 =$ _____

$7 \times 3 =$ _____ $3 \times 3 =$ _____ $3 \times 9 =$ _____ $3 \times 6 =$ _____

$3 \times 8 =$ _____ $3 \times 6 =$ _____ $3 \times 7 =$ _____ $3 \times 4 =$ _____

Write in the missing factor(s) in these factor pairs.

$\underline{3}$—(15)—___ $\underline{3}$—(27)—___ $\underline{3}$—(21)—___ $\underline{7}$—(56)—___   ___—(9)—___

___—(35)—___   ___—(36)—___   ___—(28)—___   ___—(27)—___   ___—(56)—___

___—(12)—___   ___—(24)—___   ___—(18)—___   ___—(21)—___   ___—(15)—___

Double a factor and double the product.

$2 \times 3 =$ _____	$3 \times 3 =$ _____	$3 \times 4 =$ _____	$3 \times 5 =$ _____
$4 \times 3 =$ _____	$6 \times 3 =$ _____	$3 \times 8 =$ _____	$3 \times 10 =$ _____

Multiples of 3 (2)

Sum of the Digits of multiples of 3:

If the sum of the digits of a number is 3, (or any multiple of 3), the number is a multiple of 3.

$3 \times 5 =$ _____ : $1 + 5 =$ _6_ $3 \times 6 =$ _____ : $1 + 8 =$ _____

$3 \times 7 =$ _____ : $2 + 1 =$ _____ $3 \times 9 =$ _____ : $2 + 7 =$ _____

$3 \times 4 =$ _____ : $1 + 2 =$ _____ $3 \times 8 =$ _____ : $2 + 4 =$ _____

Write in the missing factor(s) in these factor pairs.

$\underset{}{\overset{3}{\_\_}}$ (12) ____ ____ (15) ____ ____ (18) ____ ____ (21) ____ ____ (24) ____

Show common factor and factor pairs as in model.
Use only single digit factors.

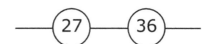

$\overset{3}{\_}$ (21) $\overset{7}{\_}$ (14) $\overset{2}{\_}$ ____ (27) ____ (36) ____   ____ (15) ____ (35) ____

____ (24) ____ (72) ____   ____ (54) ____ (30) ____   ____ (21) ____ (56) ____

____ (49) ____ (56) ____   ____ (24) ____ (56) ____   ____ (24) ____ (9) ____

____ (64) ____ (24) ____   ____ (24) ____ (15) ____   ____ (18) ____ (21) ____

____ (72) ____ (27) ____   ____ (18) ____ (63) ____   ____ (35) ____ (21) ____

Multiples of 6 (1)

Count by 6s from 6 to 72 orally and in writing. Circle the facts you know.

6	___	___	___	___	___	___	___	___	___	___	72
1×	2×	3×	4×	5×	6×	7×	8×	9×	10×	11×	12×

Double a factor and double the product.

3 × 7 = _____   3 × 4 = _____   3 × 3 = _____   3 × 5 = _____

6 × 7 = _____   6 × 4 = _____   3 × 6 = _____   6 × 5 = _____

3 × 4 = _____   3 × 6 = _____   3 × 8 = _____   3 × 10 = _____

6 × 4 = _____   6 × 6 = _____   6 × 8 = _____   6 × 10 = _____

6 × 6 = _____   6 × 8 = _____   5 × 6 = _____   3 × 6 = _____

9 × 6 = _____   4 × 6 = _____   6 × 7 = _____

> Think 3 x 7 and multiply by 2.

Write in the missing factors in these factor pairs.

—(48)—   —(24)—   —(54)—   —(36)—   —(12)—

—(18)—   —(30)—   —(42)—   —(48)—   —(54)—

Before assigning this page, have students discover factor pairs of 28, 42, 48 from their knowledge of 14, 21, 24.
- *What's 3 × 7? So what's 6 × 7? How do you know?*
- *What's 3 × 8? So what's 6 × 8?*   • *What's 2 × 7? So what's 4 × 7?*
- *What's 4 × 6? So what's 8 × 6?*
- *Are 42 and 48 easy to divide by 2? Why? (Only even digits.)*
- *Give me a factor pair of 21. (3 ×7). So is 7 also a factor of 42?*
- *Count by 12 from 12 to 48. Are these also multiples of 6? Explain. (12 has 6 as a factor.)*

Multiples of 6 (2)

Count by 6s from 6 to 72 orally and in writing:

6											72
1×	2×	3×	4×	5×	6×	7×	8×	9×	10×	11×	12×

When you multiply 6 by an EVEN number you get a multiples of 12:

    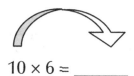

2 × 6 = _____   4 × 6 = _____   6 × 6 = _____   8 × 6 = _____   10 × 6 = _____

Look at the unit digits of the products. What do you notice?

When you multiply 6 by 4, the unit digit of the product is _____   4 × 6 = _____

When you multiply 6 by 8, the unit digit of the product is _____   8 × 6 = _____

When you multiply 6 by 6, the unit digit of the product is _____   6 × 6 = _____

When you multiply 6 by 2, the unit digit of the product is _____   2 × 6 = _____

When you multiply 6 by 12, the unit digit of the product is _____   12 × 6 = _____

Sum of the Digits.

6 = 2 × 3.   So multiples of 6 have 2 and 3 as factors. As multiples of 2, they are even.
As with all multiples of 3 the Sum of the Digits is 3, 6, or 9 (or a multiple).

Check that this applies to:

4 × 6 = __24__   _2_ + _4_ = _6_

3 × 6 = _____   ___ + ___ = _____

8 × 6 = _____   ___ + ___ = _____

7 × 6 = _____   ___ + ___ = _____

> As elsewhere, the material is best presented to students by first asking questions that help them discover and formulate patterns and connections:
>
> • 6 = 2 × 3. So what can you say about multiples of 6? Are they all even? All multiples of 3?
> • What do we know about the Sum of the Digits of multiples of 3?
>   Does that apply to multiples of 6?
> • Let's multiply 6 by an even digit.
>   Why do we get a multiple of 12? (Product inherits 6 from one factor and 2 from the other)
> • "4 times 6, 24"; "8 times 6, 48"; "6 times 6, 36."
>   So what do you notice about the unit digits?

Double a factor and double the product.

21 ⁷	24 ⁶	24 ⁸
42 ⁷	48 ⁶	48 ⁸

Show common factor and factor pairs as in model.
Use only factors from 2 to 10.

⁸ — (48) — ⁶ — (18) — ³   — (48) — (16) —   — (35) — (42) —

— (48) — (56) —   — (24) — (42) —   — (28) — (42) —

— (36) — (27) —   — (64) — (48) —   — (24) — (64) —

— (18) — (24) —   — (27) — (63) —   — (15) — (24) —

— (54) — (24) —   — (42) — (49) —   — (36) — (42) —

— (56) — (42) —   — (36) — (30) —

> This is a good time to transfer to memory of sound and rhythm the familiarity acquired with 6 times facts.

Multiples of 4 (1)

| What's 8 × 8? | _____ |

| What's one-half of 64? | _____ |

| So what's 4 × 8? | _____ |

Double a factor and double the product.

| 2 × 2 = ____ | 2 × 3 = ____ | 2 × 4 = ____ | 2 × 5 = ____ |
| 4 × 2 = ____ | 4 × 3 = ____ | 4 × 4 = ____ | 4 × 5 = ____ |

| 2 × 6 = ____ | 2 × 7 = ____ | 2 × 8 = ____ | 2 × 9 = ____ |
| 4 × 6 = ____ | 4 × 7 = ____ | 4 × 8 = ____ | 4 × 9 = ____ |

| 2 x 7 = 14, so you know 4 x 7. | 16 + 16 is 2 more than 15 + 15. | Starts with 1 less than 4. |

Use the information above to fill in the factor pairs. Use 4 as a factor:

—(12)— —(28)— —(32)— —(36)— —(8)—

—(16)— —(24)— —(20)— —(28)— —(32)—

—(36)— —(24)— —(32)— —(40)— —(16)—

Before assigning this page, have students discover 4 × 6, 4 × 7, 4 × 8
based on their knowledge of 2 × 6, 2 × 7, 2 × 8
• What's 2 × 6? So what's 4 × 6? How do you know?
• What's 2 × 8? So what's 4 × 8? (What's 15 + 15? So what's 16 + 16?)
• What's 2 × 7? So what's 4 × 7?
• 28. Is that number easy to divide by 2? Why? (Even digits).
• What do you know about 14? (2 × 7). Does this mean that 28 also has 7 as a factor?

Multiples of 4 (2)

Count by 4s from 4 to 48 orally and in writing:

$\underline{4}$	$\underline{}$	$\underline{}$	$\underline{}$	$\underline{}$	$\underline{}$	$\underline{}$	$\underline{}$	$\underline{}$	$\underline{}$	$\underline{}$	$\underline{48}$
1×	2×	3×	4×	5×	6×	7×	8×	9×	10×	11×	12×

Factor pairs.

— (8) —   — (16) —   — (32) —   — (64) —   — (24) —

— (56) —   — (21) —   — (28) —   — (12) —   — (16) —

4 — (36) —   6 — (36) —   — (20) —   — (49) —   — (81) —

Show common factor and factor pairs as in model.
Use only factors from 2 to 10.

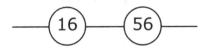 9 — (36) 4 — (28) 7 —   — (16) — (56) —   — (12) — (18) —

— (20) — (32) —   — (24) — (18) —   — (28) — (35) —

— (12) — (21) —   — (28) — (32) —   — (16) — (20) —

— (28) — (16) —   — (36) — (45) —   — (36) — (28) —

— (64) — (32) —   — (32) — (16) —   — (49) — (28) —

Multiples of 8 (1)

Help students discover that they have already studied all multiple of 8 and all essential facts from 2 × 2 to 9 × 9. They desrve to be congratulated.

Count by 8s from 8 to 96 orally and in writing:

8 ___ ___ ___ ___ ___ ___ ___ ___ ___ ___ ___ 96
1×   2×   3×   4×   5×   6×   7×   8×   9×   10× 11× 12×

What's 8 × 8? So what's 4 × 8?   "5, 6, 7, 8; ___ is 7 × 8."   Think 10 × 8 = 80 plus 2 × 8 = 16.

Double a factor and double the product.

| 4 × 8 = ____ | 6 × 4 = ____ | 3 × 8 = ____ | 10 × 8 = ____ |
| 8 × 8 = ____ | 6 × 8 = ____ | 6 × 8 = ____ | 5 × 8 = ____ |

Divisible by 8.

8 = 2 × 2 × 2. So a number that is divisible by 8 can be divided by 2 three times over.

Divide (multiply) these numbers by 2 over and over three times as modeled:

16	48	64	32	24	___	___
8	___	___	___	___	___	___
4	___	___	___	___	___	___
2	___	___	___	___	7	9

Count from 1 to 128 by doubling each number:

1   2   4   ___   ___   ___   ___   128

© Edric Cane 2020   Copying without written permission is illegal.

69

Multiples of 8 (2)

Write in the missing factors. Use 8 as a factor when possible.

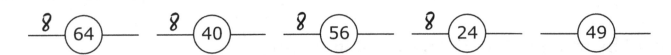

Show common factor and factor pairs as in model.
Use only factors from 2 to 10.

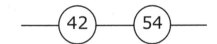

Add 8 times fact family to
ORAL practice while facts are
still present in memory.
Review fact familes 6, 7, 8, 9
to the square of these numbers.

Guided Discovery

The aim is to give students a practical experience of the ease and benefits of frequent oral/rhythmic review of essential facts. The sound and rhythm of each fact, whether spoken aloud, just whispered, or even just imagined in one's mind, is likely to have a long shelf-life in many students' memory.

We suggested reviewing facts with the smaller factor first: "*3 times 7, 21*," not also "*7 times 3, 21*." This avoids conflicting versions and shortens the time it takes to review. This is achieved by reviewing each fact family only to the square number of the family: the 6-times family is reviewed only to "*6 times 6, 36.*" Beyond the square, the fact is stated with the larger factor first: "*7 times 6, 42.*"

For further convenience, we suggest frequent review of only fact families 6, 7, 8, 9. Skipping fact families for 2, 3, 4, 5 eliminates only very simple and familiar facts. (See below the top group of facts.)

Students fill in the facts below. (Take your time.) How many facts in all?

$2 \times 2 =$ _____ $2 \times 3 =$ _____ $2 \times 4 =$ _____ $2 \times 5 =$ _____

$3 \times 3 =$ _____ $3 \times 4 =$ _____ $3 \times 5 =$ _____

$4 \times 4 =$ _____ $4 \times 5 =$ _____

$5 \times 5 =$ _____

$2 \times 6 =$ _____ $2 \times 7 =$ _____ $2 \times 8 =$ _____ $2 \times 9 =$ _____

$3 \times 6 =$ _____ $3 \times 7 =$ _____ $3 \times 8 =$ _____ $3 \times 9 =$ _____

$4 \times 6 =$ _____ $4 \times 7 =$ _____ $4 \times 8 =$ _____ $4 \times 9 =$ _____

$5 \times 6 =$ _____ $5 \times 7 =$ _____ $5 \times 8 =$ _____ $5 \times 9 =$ _____

$6 \times 6 =$ _____ $6 \times 7 =$ _____ $6 \times 8 =$ _____ $6 \times 9 =$ _____

$7 \times 7 =$ _____ $7 \times 8 =$ _____ $7 \times 9 =$ _____

$8 \times 8 =$ _____ $8 \times 9 =$ _____

$9 \times 9 =$ _____

- Discus what each column represents. Notice where each one stops.
- Discus what changes when we go beyond the square. *(Larger factor is first.)*
- How easy are the facts in the top group? Could they be skipped?
- Starting with "*2 × 6, 12…*", let students read the bottom group.
- Do it again with a finger going down the line on the back cover.
- Try again without rushing. Is that something you could soon practice regularly in not much more than a minute?

31 multiples and 36 essential facts

The 31 numbers on the right represent the 36 essential facts from 2 × 2 to 9 × 9. Oral review through conversation gives a different perspective on these facts.

Ask students (not looking at the list) to search their mind for different categories of facts, giving both products and factor pairs.

Identify each category.
Give the factor pairs. Discuss.

- The 6 essential facts higher than 50.
- The 5 facts in the 40s.
- The 4 products and 5 facts in the 30s.
- The 6 products and 7 facts in the 20s.
- The 6 numbers and 9 facts in the 10s.

- The 5 products that have two different single-digit factor pairs.
- The 4 products and 5 facts with 8 as the unit digit.
- The 4 products and 6 facts with 6 as the unit digit.
- Products with 3, with 7 as the unit digit.
- Products with 5 as the unit digit.

- Give easy double/half pairs and their factor pairs.
- Give the square of digits from 2 to 9.
- For each square, give a product 1 less than the square and its factor pair. What do you notice?
- Starting with 1, double each number all the way to 128.

- Copy this list and cross out different categories or families of facts that are already familiar.
- Discuss facts that remain less familiar.
- Continue short, frequent, oral reviews of one or all essential fact families by giving a full statement of each fact ("1 times 7, 7; 2 times 7, 14; ...") as suggested on the previous page or by running through the products only ("7, 14, 21, 28 ...") as prompted by a finger going down one of the lines on the back cover.

4	
6	
8	
9	
10	
12	12
14	
15	
16	16
18	18
20	
21	
24	24
25	
27	
28	
30	
32	
35	
36	36
40	
42	
45	
48	
49	
54	
56	
63	
64	
72	
81	

Times Squares

2-31(1)

Fill in all the cells:
Factors from 2 to 9
in grey cells;
Corresponding products
in white cells.

	3							
3								
					49			
				48			24	
								4
9								
			25					
		24		32		36		
	24							

What factor do 24 and 56 have in common?

2-31(2)

		27	54					
				20	35			
					8	20		
	24							
	56							
							18	
							72	
					42			

What factor do 14 and 35 have in common?

Messed-Up Times Squares

2-32(1)

Fill in all the cells:
Factors from 2 to 9
in grey cells;
Corresponding products
in white cells.

							6	
					49			
								4
				9				
	64							
		24			42			
			81					
	25							
	32							

2-32(2)

							32
			56				
	15		18			27	
				42			
				28			
						36	
			16				
10		15					

Factor Chain

Show **common factors** and **factor pairs**.
Begin with factor pair of top left bubble. Use only factors from 2 to 9.

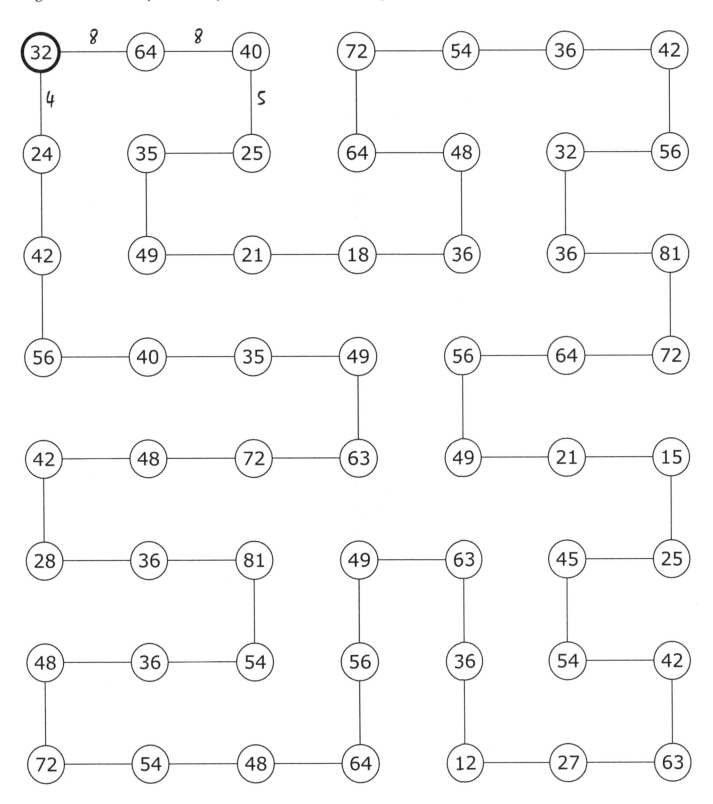

Factor Chain

 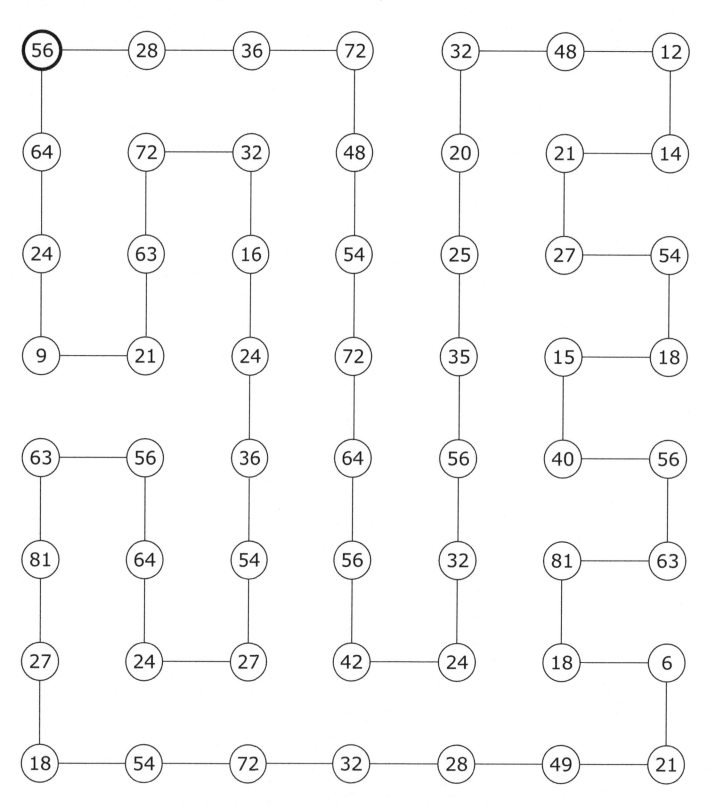

Show **common factors** and **factor pairs**.
Begin with factor pair of top left bubble. Use only factors from 2 to 9.

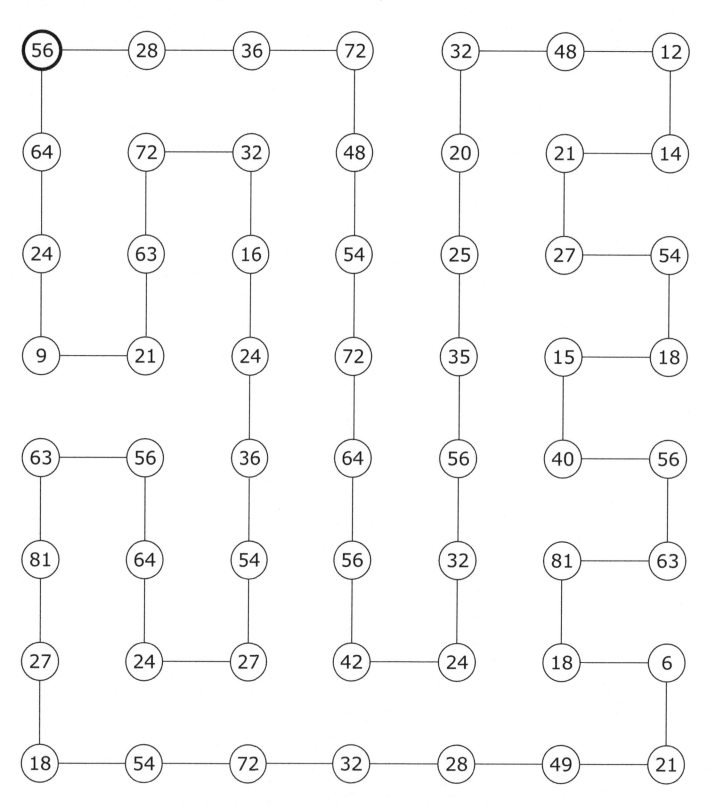

Factor Chain

Show **common factors** and **factor pairs**.
Begin with factor pair of top left bubble. Use only factors from 2 to 9.

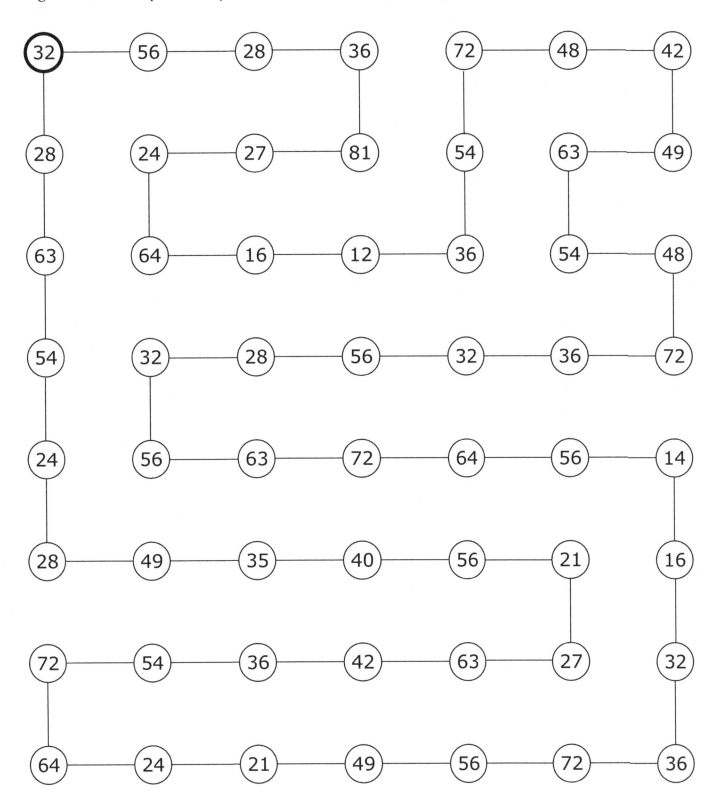

Factor Chain

Show **common factors** and **factor pairs**.
Begin with factor pair of top left bubble. Use only factors from 2 to 9.

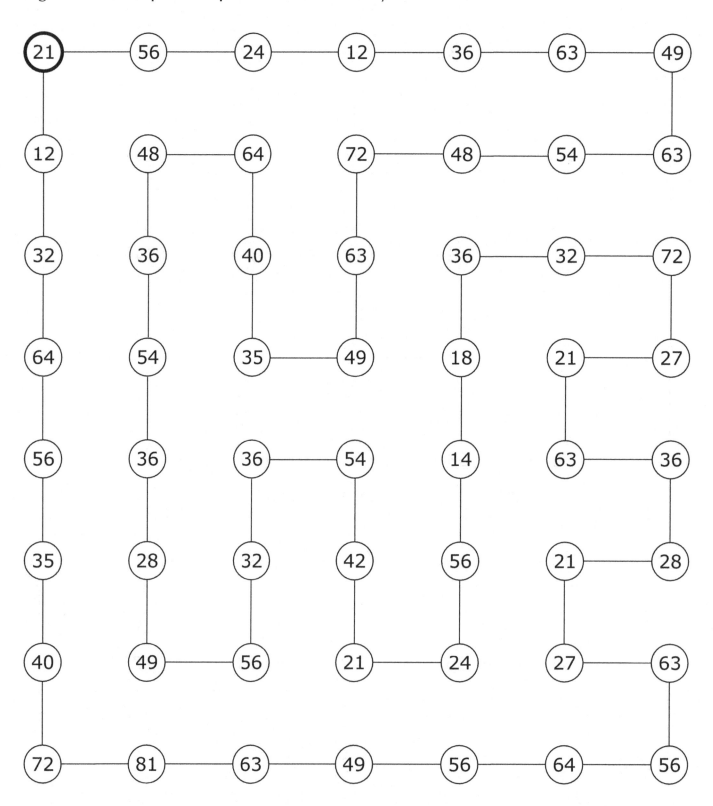

Factor Chain

Show **common factors** and **factor pairs.**
Begin with factor pair of top left bubble. Use only factors from 2 to 9.

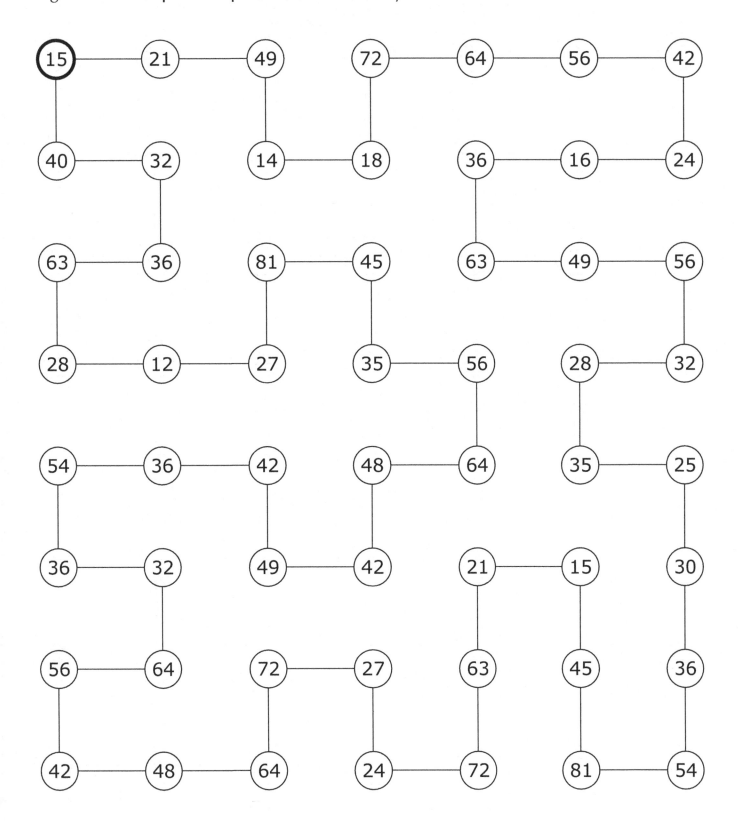

Factor Chain

Show **common factors** and **factor pairs**.
Use only factors from 2 to 9.

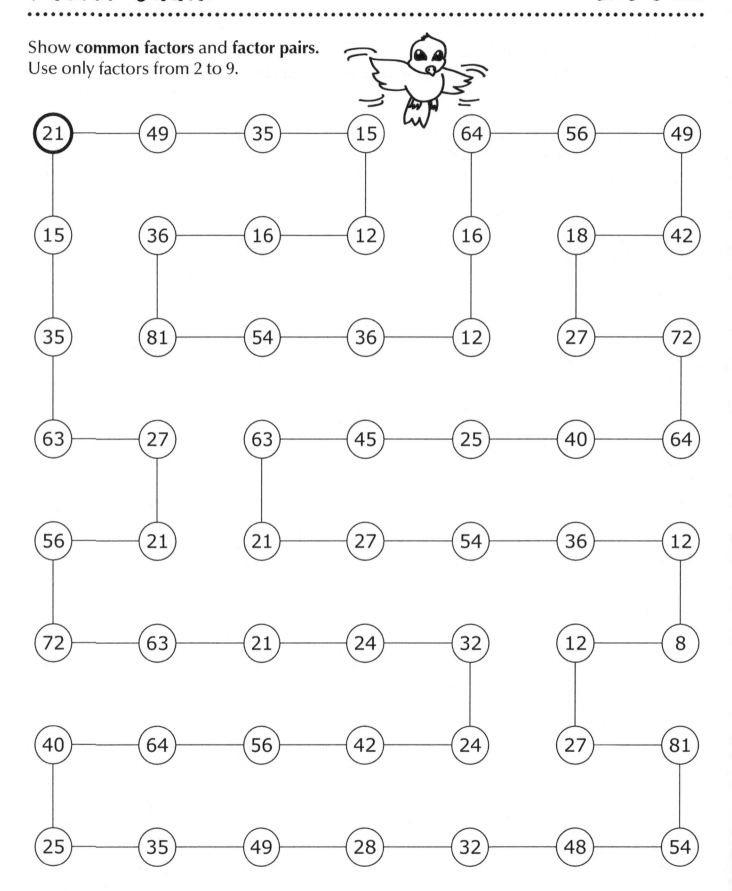

LEVEL 3 Taking Stock

Level 3 provides continued practice on our 36 essential facts and looks at various characteristics of factors — prime factors, common factors, Greatest Common Factors (GCF), Least Common Multiples (LCM) —, how factors can be grouped, how their features apply to fractions. In the process, students broaden their understanding of numbers at work. Fact families of 11 and 12 are added to the single-digit fact families already studied.

Guided Conversation

As an introduction to Level 3, an open-ended conversation with student or class. Objective: Taking stock of what facts have been learned. Suggested outline:

Fill in the blank cells in this Times Square. They show the facts that we have studied in Levels 1 and 2.

Why are they essential?

How would you rate your familiarity with these 36 facts?

What remains a challenge?

Many facts have a double/half connection with other facts. Give examples.

What strategies, what tools, what patterns and connections help you learn and remember?

1	2	3	4	5	6	7	8	9
2	4	6						
3	6							
4								
5								
6								
7								
8								
9								

How long does it take you to review orally fact families 6, 7, 8 and 9? (See Level 2, 2-29.)

Guided Conversation

As students are looking at the Times Squares on the previous page, let's explore its structure and help them experience the notions of symmetry and of an axis of symmetry.

> What's 3 × 7? Where do you see that on your Times Square? (On previous page.) Why do you find it twice?

I find it in Column 3/Row 7 and in Row 3/Column 7.

> Circle (color) those two products and join them with a line.

> In the same way circle and join the products of 2 × 4, 3 × 7, 3 × 9, 6 × 8, and 8 × 9.

> What about the squares: 3 × 3, 7 × 7, 8 × 8? Why do they appear only once?

No difference between Row 3/Column 3 and Column 3/Row 3.

> Circle (color) those square numbers and draw a line along the diagonal of the square, from 1 to 81.

1	2	3	4	5	6	7	8	9
2	4	6	⑧	10	12	14	16	18
3	6	✗	12	15	18	㉑	24	㉗
4	⑧	12	16	20	24	28	32	36
5	10	15	20	25	30	35	40	45
6	12	18	24	30	36	42	㊽	54
7	14	㉑	28	35	42	49	56	63
8	16	24	32	40	㊽	56	64	㉒
9	18	㉗	36	45	54	63	㉒	81

> What words can describe what you see?

(Students or teacher introduce the words "Symmetry" and "Axis of symmetry.")

> If you fold the Times Square along its axis of symmetry, what do you notice about the position of 8, 21, 27, 48?

8 covers 8; 21 is over 21.

> Where do you see symmetries in nature?

Human face, butterfly, leaves.

> Sketch a leaf or butterfly showing an axis of symmetry.

We may also explore figures with more than one axes of symmetry.

Prime Numbers

Guided Discovery

Ask questions to help students discover. Ask students to give examples that illustrate and explain.

- Write a factor pair for 6. Write a factor pair for 7. What's different?
- Can you write 7 as the product of two numbers? *(7 × 1)* Does that break 7 up?
- Can you think of other numbers that cannot be broken up? *(2, 3, 5, 7, 11…)*. ***Prime numbers.***
- Give numbers that can be written as factor pairs of two other numbers? ***Composite numbers.***
- What are the first prime numbers? The first composite numbers? What are their prime factors?
- Give two factor pairs for 36. Find the factors of the two factors.
- 36 has different factor pairs. Does it have different sets of prime factors?

5 cannot be *broken up* into factors. It is a prime number.

1 — (5) — 5

The first prime numbers are circled.

By definition, 2 is the only multiple of 2 that is prime.

3 is the only multiple of 3 that is prime.

7 is the only multiple of 7 that is prime. Why?

2	3	4	5	6	7	8	9	10
11	12	13	14	15	16	17	18	19
20	21	22	23	24	25	26	27	28
29	30	31	32	33	34	35	36	37

Numbers that are not prime are called ***composite.*** They can be ***broken up*** into factors.
1 is neither prime nor composite.

To find the prime factors of a composite number, write it first as a convenient factor pair:

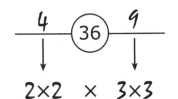

4 — (36) — 9

2×2 × 3×3

35 — (350) — 10

5×7 × 2×5

The prime factors of a number are like fingerprints for people.
Each number has a unique set of prime factors, and only one such set.

Prime Factors

Show single-digit factor pairs. Then show all the prime factors as in model.

4 — (24) — 6 ↓ ↓ 2×2 × 3×2	3 — (27) — 9 3 × 3×3	— (36) — _____ × _____
— (35) — _____ × _____	— (42) — _____ × _____	— (45) — _____ × _____
— (54) — _____ × _____	— (27) — _____ × _____	— (28) — _____ × _____
— (32) — _____ × _____	— (63) — _____ × _____	— (56) — _____ × _____
— (21) — _____ × _____	— (81) — _____ × _____	— (48) — _____ × _____
— (16) — _____ × _____	— (32) — _____ × _____	With applications such as these students keep reviewing the 36 essential facts they most need to know.

Prime Factors

Show a factor pair. Then show all the prime factors as in model.

$\overset{8}{\underset{\downarrow}{}}$ (72) $\overset{9}{\underset{\downarrow}{}}$ 2×2×2× 3×3	——(28)—— ___ × ___	——(32)—— ___ × ___
——(100)—— ___ × ___	——(21)—— ___ × ___	——(12)—— ___ × ___
——(63)—— ___ × ___	——(36)—— ___ × ___	——(45)—— ___ × ___
——(56)—— ___ × ___	——(60)—— ___ × ___	——(18)—— ___ × ___
——(81)—— ___ × ___	——(16)—— ___ × ___	——(90)—— ___ × ___
——(24)—— ___ × ___	——(42)—— ___ × ___	——(54)—— ___ × ___

Prime Factors

As in model: **Find prime factors. Put them in order. Use exponents.**

$$\overset{8}{\underset{\downarrow}{}}\;\overset{}{\boxed{72}}\;\overset{9}{\underset{\downarrow}{}}$$

$$2\times2\times2\times\;3\times3$$

$$2^3\;\times\;3^2$$

Order the prime factors of 72 from smallest to largest. Use exponents.

$$\overset{6}{\underset{\downarrow}{}}\;\overset{}{\boxed{24}}\;\overset{4}{\underset{\downarrow}{}}$$

$$2\times3\;\times\;2\times2$$

$$2^3\;\times\;3$$

$\boxed{81}$

$\boxed{64}$

$\boxed{63}$

$\times$

$\boxed{56}$

$\boxed{54}$

$\boxed{49}$

$\boxed{48}$

$\boxed{42}$

$\boxed{40}$

$\boxed{36}$

$\boxed{35}$

$\boxed{32}$

$\boxed{28}$

$\boxed{27}$

Prime Factors

As in model: Find prime factors. Put them in order. Use exponents.

$$\overset{6}{\downarrow}\ \ \overset{}{54}\ \ \overset{9}{\downarrow}$$

2×3 × 3×3

2   ×   3³

—32—

—81—

—16—

—24—

—72—

—28—

—63—

—64—

—48—

—56—

—36—

—54—

—45—

—27—

—49—

—18—

—42—

© Edric Cane 2020   Copying without written permission is illegal.

Grouping (1)

Guided Discovery/Activity

Below, we suggest prompts and student responses. Alternative numbers: 54, 48, 36.

| Write a factor pair of 72 and then its prime factors. |

$$\frac{8}{\downarrow} \, (72) \, \frac{9}{\downarrow}$$

| Copy prime factors on small pieces of paper. |

$$2 \times 2 \times 2 \times \; 3 \times 3$$

| Make two groups of those prime factors in as many different ways as you can. |

| Record each combination and write as factor pairs. |

We expect the combinations that follow, each one then written as a factor pair of 72.

2	$\times$	$2 \times 2 \times 3 \times 3$		$2 \; (72) \; 36$
3	$\times$	$2 \times 2 \times 2 \times 3$		$3 \; (72) \; 24$
2×2	$\times$	$2 \times 3 \times 3$		$4 \; (72) \; 18$
2×3	$\times$	$2 \times 2 \times 3$		$6 \; (72) \; 12$
3×3	$\times$	$2 \times 2 \times 2$		$9 \; (72) \; 8$

Ask questions to help students discover. Ask students for examples that illustrate and explain.
- How many factor pairs did you find for 72?
- Do you get a different set of prime factors if you start with a different factor pair of 72?
- Numbers have only one set of prime factors. So why do we have different factor pairs?
  We get different factor pairs by grouping them differently.
- What essential multiples have two different single-digit factor pairs?   *12, 16, 18, 24, 36.*
- Show different factor pairs of 48; find the prime factors; group them differently.
- Comment on the factor pairs of 35.   *Both factors are prime factors. Only true option.*
- Comment on the factor pairs of 13.   *Only 1 × 13. 13 is a prime number.*

Grouping (2)

Guided Discovery

These are the prime factors of a number.

What can you say about that number?

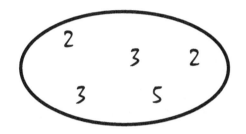

Students are expected to list some factors and give some consequences:

It has 2 as a factor, so it is even.
It has 2 twice as a factor, so it can be divided by 4.
It has 3 twice, so it is a multiple of 9. The sum of its digits is 9 (or a multiple.)
It has 2 and 5 as factors, so it is a multiple of 10. The unit digit is 0.

Cover up factors 2 and 5.   What is left?

2, 3, and 3. That's 2 × 9 = 18.

So what is the number?

10 x 18 = 180

Activity

Find eight factor pairs of 180 by breaking the prime factors into two groups such as:
$180 = (2 \times 3 \times 3) \times (2 \times 5) = 18 \times 10$. Write them in some organized list on that model.

$$180 = 2 \times (2 \times 3 \times 3 \times 5) = 2 \times 90$$
$$180 = 3 \times (2 \times 2 \times 3 \times 5) = 3 \times 60$$
$$180 = (2 \times 2) \times (3 \times 3 \times 5) = 4 \times 45$$
$$180 = 5 \times (2 \times 2 \times 3 \times 3) = 5 \times 36$$
$$180 = (2 \times 3) \times (2 \times 3 \times 5) = 6 \times 30$$
$$180 = (3 \times 3) \times (2 \times 2 \times 5) = 9 \times 20$$
$$180 = (2 \times 5) \times (2 \times 3 \times 3) = 10 \times 18$$
$$180 = (2 \times 2 \times 3) \times (3 \times 5) = 12 \times 15$$

This kind of conversation can be repeated using other numbers, such as the prime factors of 240, 480, or 900.

With 900, students can be helped to notice that the factors come in pairs, so the number is a square. Breaking up those pairs leads to $900 = 30 \times 30 = 30^2$.

Jumping Factors

Guided Discovery. Prompt students to gradually implement the changes:

Before   After

Give a factor pair of 42.

42   6 42 7

Find prime factors:

$\times$ $2 \times 3 \times 7$

Regroup factors differently:

$42 =$ $②\times③\times⑦ = 2 \times 21$

Other option?   *Regroup 2 x 7.* $42 =$ $③\times②\times⑦ = 3 \times 14$

Give three factor pairs of 42: $42 = 6 \times 7 = 2 \times 21 = 3 \times 14$

Now let's do this again with shortcuts:

$6 = 2 \times 3$. Let's move factor 2 to the right:

We regroup $2 \times 7 = 14$. New factor pair:

42   42 6 42 7 $2 \rightarrow$ 3 42 14

Another option? *Yes. Let's move the factor 3.*

You want to move 3 to the right:

$3 \times 7 = 21$. New factor pair of 42?

6 42 7 $3 \rightarrow$ 2 42 21

Now let's do this again with 36.
Tell me what you want to do.

Make factor 2 jump to the left:

What's the new factor pair?

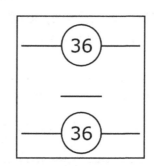

36   36 9 36 4 $2 \leftarrow$ 18 36 2

Jumping Factors

On this first page, all the products in the bubbles are even. They have 2 as a factor. Make that factor 2 jump from one side to the other.

1) Find a familiar factor pair using factors between 2 and 10:

   $\dfrac{6}{}$ (42) $\dfrac{7}{}$

2) 6 = 2 × 3. Make the factor 2 jump to the other side.

   2 × 3 (42) 7

   Divide 6 by 2.   Multiply 7 by 2.

   2 →

3) We have a less familiar factor pair of 42: 42 = 3 × 14

   $\dfrac{3}{}$ (42) $\dfrac{14}{}$

$\dfrac{6}{}$ (48) $\dfrac{8}{}$

Write in the jumping factor. 2 →

$\dfrac{3}{}$ (48) $\dfrac{16}{}$

$\dfrac{9}{}$ (54) $\dfrac{6}{}$

← 2

$\dfrac{18}{}$ (54) $\dfrac{3}{}$

(28)

—

(28)

---

(32)

—

(32)

(100)

—

(100)

---

(56)

—

(56)

(90)

—

(90)

(36)

—

(36)

Jumping Factors

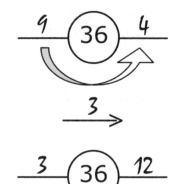

1) Find a familiar factor pair using factors between 2 and 10:

2) Then find a factor of one of the factors. Make it jump to the other side.

   Here, we choose to make the factor 3 jump to the other side. We get 3 × 4 = 12.
   We have a less familiar factor pair of 36: 36 = 3 × 12:

Show factor pairs and jumping factor, as in model.

7 —(63)— 9

3 ←

21 —(63)— 3

—(80)—

———

—(80)—

—(54)—

———

—(54)—

—(45)—

———

—(45)—

—(56)—

2

—(56)—

—(72)—

2

—(72)—

—(72)—

3

—(72)—

—(81)—

———

—(81)—

Jumping Factors

Find a familiar factor pair using factors between 2 and 10.
Find a factor of one of the factors. Write the jumping factor down and make it jump to the other side to make a different factor pair. Add arrow as in model.

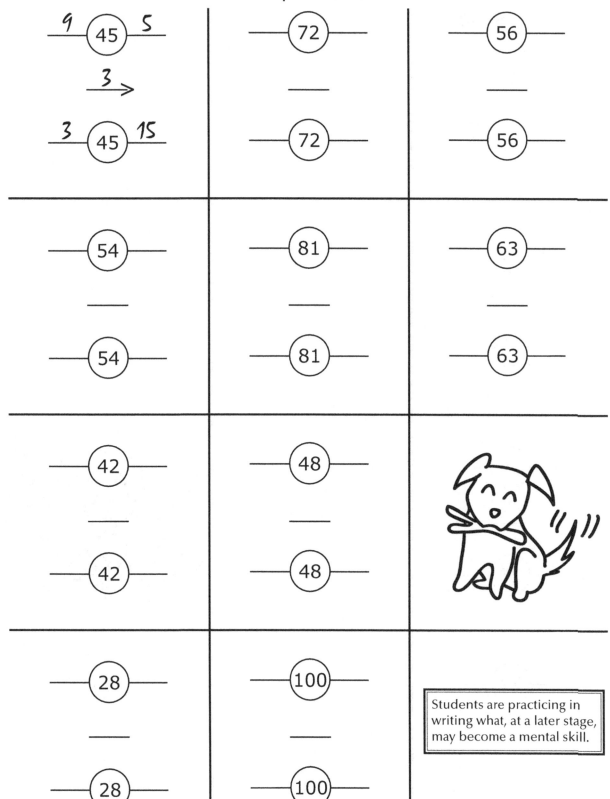

9 —(45)— 5

3 →

3 —(45)— 15

—(72)—

—(72)—

—(56)—

—(56)—

—(54)—

—(54)—

—(81)—

—(81)—

—(63)—

—(63)—

—(42)—

—(42)—

—(48)—

—(48)—

—(28)—

—(28)—

—(100)—

—(100)—

Students are practicing in writing what, at a later stage, may become a mental skill.

Jumping Factors

Find a familiar factor pair using factors between 2 and 10.
Find a factor of one of the factors. Write the jumping factor down and make it jump to the other side to make a different factor pair. See model.

9 —(90)— 10

← 2

18 —(90)— 5

—(45)—

——

—(45)—

—(63)—

——

—(63)—

—(56)—

——

—(56)—

—(36)—

——

—(36)—

—(60)—

——

—(60)—

—(28)—

——

—(28)—

—(48)—

——

—(48)—

—(72)—

——

—(72)—

—(54)—

——

—(54)—

—(42)—

——

—(42)—

Changing the Order of Operations

in a series of multiplications and divisions

Guided Discovery

It is expected that parent/teachers will discuss this material with students.

- In a series of multiplications and divisions you can always do the calculations in order from left to right.
- Sometimes there is a more convenient order.
- The key to knowing what you can do and cannot do is using or imagining BUBBLES.

In the following example, if we do the calculation in order from left to right, intermediate calculations include inconvenient decimals (56 is not divisible by 3). If we try to change the order, there are many things that we cannot do. We cannot switch 3 and 21. We cannot multiply 3 × 21. But, there is an easier way than from left to right.

| What does this expression tell us to do? | $56 \div 3 \times 21 \div 8 = \underline{49}$ |

Take 56, divide by 3, multiply by 21, divide by 8.

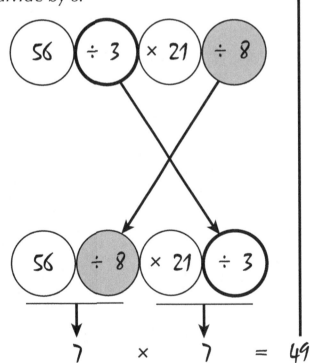

| Let's put each instruction inside a bubble. |

| What's a factor pair of 56? *(56 = 7 × 8.)*
So it is easy to divide 56 by 8 but not by 3. |

| What's a factor pair of 21? *(21 = 3 x 7.)*
So it is easy to divide 21 by 3 but not by 8. |

| Let's change the order of these bubbles to group operations that are easy. |

| Now we can group and do the calculations mentally. |

- Let students experience the difficulty of doing the operations from left to right.
- Help them notice that 56 is divisible by 8 and 21 by 3.
- Model drawing bubbles and changing the order of the bubbles.
- Suggest grouping and solving the sequence mentally.
- Real or imagined, bubbles link a number and its operation.

Changing the Order of Operations

3-16 ⊞

in a series of multiplications and divisions (Continued from previous page)

Your turn: First, put your pen just behind each number as modeled and draw a bubble around each number *and the sign in front of it*.

Then, change the order of the bubbles and group them as convenient.

$\boxed{27}\; \boxed{\div\; 4}\; \div\; 3\; \times\; 28\; =$ _____

○ ○ ○ ○

_____ × _____ = _____

$(27 \div 3 \times 28 \div 4 = 9 \times 7 = 63)$

64 ÷ 9 × 27 ÷ 8 = _____   90 × 17 ÷ 9 = _____

○ ○ ○ ○   ○ ○ ○

_____ = _____   _____ = _____

You draw all the bubbles:

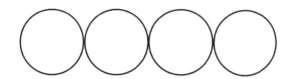

16 ÷ 9 ÷ 8 × 27 = _____   21 × 8 ÷ 7 = _____

_____ = _____   _____ = _____

Changing the Order of Operations

in a series of multiplications and divisions

Change the order of the calculations:

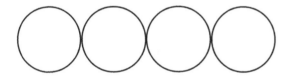

$$\underline{\quad 4 \quad} \times \underline{\quad 4 \quad} = \underline{\quad 16 \quad}$$

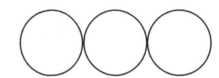

$$\underline{\qquad\qquad} = \underline{\quad\quad}$$

$$56 \times 16 \div 7 \div 4 = \underline{\quad\quad}$$

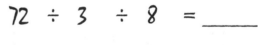

$$\underline{\qquad\qquad\qquad\qquad} = \underline{\quad\quad}$$

$$64 \times 7 \div 8 = \underline{\quad\quad}$$

$$\underline{\qquad\qquad\qquad\qquad} = \underline{\quad\quad}$$

$$45 \div 7 \times 21 \div 5 = \underline{\quad\quad}$$

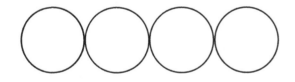

$$\underline{\qquad\qquad\qquad\qquad} = \underline{\quad\quad}$$

$$72 \div 3 \div 8 = \underline{\quad\quad}$$

$$\underline{\qquad\qquad\qquad\qquad} = \underline{\quad\quad}$$

The purpose of pages such as this one is made clear in the title: here, acquiring the ability to move numbers around in a series of multiplications and divisions by linking numbers with the operation sign that defines their function. But throughout such pages, an additional objective remains manipulating and becoming ever more familiar with essential multiplication facts. The two objectives are not exclusive of one another, quite the contrary.

in a series of multiplications and divisions

Use bubbles to change the order of the calculations:

$(49)(\div 9)(\times 54)(\div 7) = $ _____

$(\ )(\ )(\ )(\ )$

_____ = _____

$(24)(\times 9)(\div 8) = \underline{27}$

$(24)(\div 8)(\times 9)$

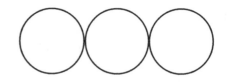

$\underline{\quad 3 \quad} \times \underline{\quad 9 \quad} = \underline{27}$

$18 \div 8 \div 3 \times 32 = $ _____

$(\ )(\ )(\ )(\ )$

_____ = _____

$9 \div 8 \times 56 = $ _____

$(\ )(\ )(\ )$

_____ = _____

$32 \div 7 \div 4 \times 63 = $ _____

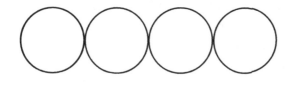

_____ = _____

$4 \div 7 \times 28 = $ _____

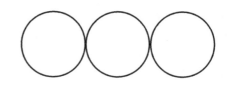

_____ = _____

You can change the order of the bubbles, but:

- A bubble with the ÷ sign cannot be put in an initial position (in first place) in an expression or in a grouping: ÷ 8 × 32 does not make sense,
- A number in an initial position (in first place) does not have an operation sign. The multiplication sign needs to be added if we change its position.

Guided Discovery. Discuss this material with students.

> This material applies to sequences of multiplications and divisions **and also sequences of additions and subtractions.** It does not apply when multiplications/divisions are combined with additions/subtractions.

$$(8)(\div 10)(\times 3)(\times 5) = 12$$

Whatever its position, each sign/number combination (each bubble) contributes its own multiplying or dividing power to the final answer. This is why it can be moved around quite freely:

- Whatever its position, $(\times 3)$ multiplies the final value by 3. We don't just have a 3, we have a 3 that multiplies by 3. We can't change it into a 3 that divides by 3. Without $\times 3$, the answer would be 3 times smaller:

$$(8)(\div 10)(\times\!\!\!/\,3)(\times 5) = 4$$

- Whatever its position, $(\div 10)$ divides the final value by 10. We don't just have a 10, we have a 10 that divides by 10. We can't change it into a 10 that multiplies by 10. Without $\div 10$, the answer would be 10 times larger:

$$(8)(\div\!\!\!/\,10)(\times 3)(\times 5) = 120$$

In a series of multiplications and divisions, just moving numbers around could change a 10 that divides into a 10 that multiplies. This is not acceptable. Bubbles help us see numbers intimately linked to the operation sign in front of them . They help us see a series of operations as instructions to "Multiply by 3!", "Divide by 10!" These instructions affect the final answer whatever their position and can be moved around quite freely.

> ## Note:
> Multiplying or dividing both sides of an equation by the same amount—or adding and subtracting the same amount from both sides—is the most fundamental process of algebraic transformations. A mind accustomed to focusing, not just on numbers (as may occur when students rely on the properties of operations to decide what can and cannot be moved), but instead on the sign/number combination that gives meaning to a number, that mind is better prepared to accept and understand the procedures of algebra.

Number Talk

Here, we use the format of Number Talk (mostly questions) to help students discover.

| How many times 9 is that? | **10 × 9** | *10 times 9.* |

| Write it as a series of additions. | 9 + 9 + 9 + 9 + 9 + 9 + 9 + 9 + 9 + 9 |

| You've got 10 x 9 as a series of additions. Change it to 13 × 9. | 9 + 9 + 9 + 9 + 9 + 9 + 9 + 9 + 9 + 9 + 9 + 9 + 9 |

| How many times did you add 9 in all? | *13 times.* |

| Circle "10 × 9" and "3 × 9." | (9 + 9 + 9 + 9 + 9 + 9 + 9 + 9 + 9 + 9) + (9 + 9 + 9) |

| What's 10 × 9? | **90** |

| What's 3 × 9? | **27** |

| What's 90 + 27? | **117** |

| How did you add these numbers? | An option: *"27 is 10 + 17. I added 10 to 90 to get 100 and 17 more to add 27."* |

| So what's 13 × 9? | **117** | (There are often other mental options.) |

| How did you find 13 × 9? | *I added 10 × 9 and 3 × 9.* |

Take your time. What's 15 × 9? (Well, what's 10 × 9? 5 × 9?) What's 12 × 7? What's 12 × 9?

This conversation initially just strengthens students' understanding of multiplication as repeat addition, bringing the obvious meaning to consciousness as opposed to just taking it for granted. Only then are we truly able to help students discover and experience that they know more than they ever thought they did. "What's 13 × 9?" would baffle many at this stage without the initial questions as most would look in vain in the memory part of their brain for the answer instead of reaching out to its thinking ability. Now it becomes a first step that, carefully nurtured over time, may mature into a natural understanding that 9 × 307 is 2700 + 63, for instance, or that 12 × 41 is 410 + 82.

11 Times Facts

Guided Discovery

The essential multiplication facts (single digits to 9 × 9) are our constant priority as they allow us to multiply any other numbers. But we may want to spend some time looking at multiples of 11 and 12. Some patterns and connections may help us remember them. Choose your favorites.

Discuss patterns and connections.

$1 \times 11 = 11$
$2 \times 11 = 22$
$3 \times 11 = 33$
$4 \times 11 = 44$
$5 \times 11 = 55$
$6 \times 11 = 66$
$7 \times 11 = 77$
$8 \times 11 = 88$
$9 \times 11 = 99$

$10 \times 11 = 110$

$11 \times 11 = 121$
$12 \times 11 = 132$
$13 \times 11 = 143$
$14 \times 11 = 154$

Using whatever strategy you choose (addition? Multiplication?), make a vertical list of multiples of 11 from 1 × 11 to 14 × 11.

Describe the pattern you get when you multiply 11 by a single-digit number.

Is that part of the pattern you always have when multiplying a number by 10?

Can you find a pattern for: 11 × 11 | 12 × 11 | 13 × 11 | 14 × 11?

Hundred and unit digits:	1 1	1 2	1 3	1 4.
Check 10s digit.	2	3	4	5
	121	132	143	154

Does the pattern apply to 11 × 43?

Yes, and to 11 × 81 = 891

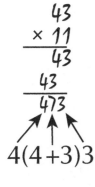

$$4(4+3)3$$

The pattern is so simple that it is a shame not to notice it.

But it does not apply to all 2-digit numbers. Why not?

The simple pattern applies only when the sum of the two digits (here 4 + 3) is a 1-digit number (9 or smaller). If the sum is 10 or larger, the need to carry over messes things up.

Apply the pattern to:

$11 \times 27 = \underline{297}$ $11 \times 81 = \underline{\hphantom{000}}$

$11 \times 53 = \underline{\hphantom{000}}$ $11 \times 11 = \underline{\hphantom{000}}$

$11 \times 25 = \underline{\hphantom{000}}$ $11 \times 12 = \underline{\hphantom{000}}$

12 Times Facts

Guided Discovery

Discuss patterns and connections. Which ones help you remember?

$1 \times 12 = 12$
$2 \times 12 = 24$
$3 \times 12 = 36$
$4 \times 12 = 48$

1 times 12 begins with 1.
2 times 12 begins with 2.
3 times 12 begins with 3.
4 times 12 begins with 4.

Add:	12	12	12	12
		12	12	12
			12	12
				12
	12	24	36	48

$5 \times 12 = 60$
$6 \times 12 = 72$
$7 \times 12 = 84$
$8 \times 12 = 96$
$9 \times 12 = 108$

5 times 12 begins with 6.
6 times 12 begins with 7.
7 times 12 begins with 8.
8 times 12 begins with 9.
9 times 12 begins with 10.

$5 \times 12 = 60$
$6 \times 12 = 60 + 12$
$7 \times 12 = 60 + 24$
$8 \times 12 = 60 + 36$
$9 \times 12 = 60 + 48$

$10 \times 12 = 120$ Part of the pattern when multiplying by 10.

$11 \times 12 = 132$ Think of pattern to multiply by 11.

$12 \times 12 = 144$ A dozen dozens. 12^2. An important fact to memorize.

Factor Chain practice.

Uses many multiples of 11 and 12.

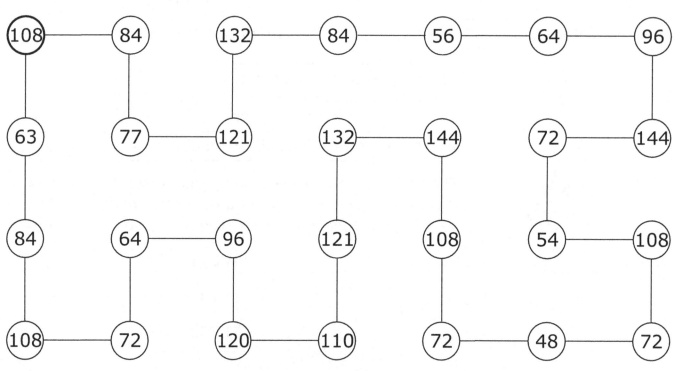

Multiples of 12

Count by 12s from 12 to 144 orally and in writing:

$\underset{1\times}{12}$ $\underset{2\times}{\rule{2em}{0.4pt}}$ $\underset{3\times}{\rule{2em}{0.4pt}}$ $\underset{4\times}{\rule{2em}{0.4pt}}$ $\underset{5\times}{\rule{2em}{0.4pt}}$ $\underset{6\times}{\rule{2em}{0.4pt}}$ $\underset{7\times}{\rule{2em}{0.4pt}}$ $\underset{8\times}{\rule{2em}{0.4pt}}$ $\underset{9\times}{\rule{2em}{0.4pt}}$ $\underset{10\times}{\rule{2em}{0.4pt}}$ $\underset{11\times}{\rule{2em}{0.4pt}}$ $\underset{12\times}{144}$

As you count orally (many times?), listen to the unit digit increase by 2:
   "12, 24, 36, 48, 60, 72, 84..."   listen to: "2, 4, 6, 8, 0, 2, 4..."

$5 \times 12 = 60$

$6 = 5 + 1$ $6 \times 12 = 60 + \rule{4em}{0.4pt} = \rule{4em}{0.4pt}$

$7 = 5 + 2$ $7 \times 12 = 60 + \rule{4em}{0.4pt} = \rule{4em}{0.4pt}$

$8 = 5 + 3$ $8 \times 12 = 60 + \rule{4em}{0.4pt} = \rule{4em}{0.4pt}$

$9 = 5 + 4$ $9 \times 12 = 60 + \rule{4em}{0.4pt} = \rule{4em}{0.4pt}$ $108 + 12 = \rule{4em}{0.4pt}$

Unit digits

$8 \times 2 = \rule{4em}{0.4pt}$ $8 \times 12 = \rule{4em}{0.4pt}$ Both unit digits are $\rule{4em}{0.4pt}$

$6 \times 2 = \rule{4em}{0.4pt}$ $6 \times 12 = \rule{4em}{0.4pt}$ Both unit digits are $\rule{4em}{0.4pt}$

$2 \times 2 = \rule{4em}{0.4pt}$ $12 \times 12 = \rule{4em}{0.4pt}$ Both unit digits are $\rule{4em}{0.4pt}$

$9 \times 2 = \rule{4em}{0.4pt}$ $9 \times 12 = \rule{4em}{0.4pt}$ Both unit digits are $\rule{4em}{0.4pt}$

$7 \times 2 = \rule{4em}{0.4pt}$ $7 \times 12 = \rule{4em}{0.4pt}$ Both unit digits are $\rule{4em}{0.4pt}$

Write in the factor pairs. Use 12 as a factor

  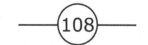

$6 \times 12 = \rule{4em}{0.4pt}$ $9 \times 12 = \rule{4em}{0.4pt}$ $11 \times 12 = \rule{4em}{0.4pt}$ $8 \times 12 = \rule{4em}{0.4pt}$

$12 \times 12 = \rule{4em}{0.4pt}$ $11 \times 11 = \rule{4em}{0.4pt}$ $7 \times 12 = \rule{4em}{0.4pt}$ $9 \times 11 = \rule{4em}{0.4pt}$

Factors

Guided Discovery. Use prompts as needed for open-ended discussion.

Show the different factor pairs of 12:

3 (12) 4   2 (12) 6   1 (12) 12

It helps to think of a number as a factor of itself and that all numbers have 1 as a factor.

Show the different ways of dividing 12 with no remainder:

$12 \div 3 = 4.$ $12 \div 2 = 6.$ $12 \div 12 = 1.$
$12 \div 4 = 3.$ $12 \div 6 = 2.$ $12 \div 1 = 12.$

12 is divisible by 1, 2, 3, 4, 6, and 12. The quotient is the other number in the factor pair. All numbers are divisible (no remainder) by all their factors.

You have 12 dollar bills. How can you divide them equally between people?

3 people, 4 dollars each.   *2 people, 6 dollars each.*   *12 people, 1 dollar each.*
4 people, 3 dollars each.   *6 people, 2 dollars each.*   *All 12 dollars to just 1 person.*

Using a grid, draw three different rectangles that have an area of 12 small squares (cells.) Label each rectangle with a factor-pair of 12.

$12 = 1 \times 12.$
$12 = 2 \times 6.$
$12 = 3 \times 4.$

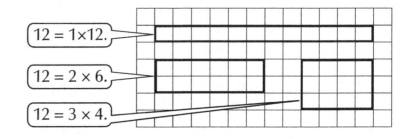

1   2   ③   4   5   ⑥   7   8   ⑨   10   11   ⑫   13

Circle the multiples of 3.   Did you circle 12?   Do you reach 12 when you count by 4s?
Do you reach 12 when you count by 5s? By 7s?   Why? / Why not?   *(Not factors of 12.)*

With finger, jump to 12 by 3s. How many jumps? What factor pair of 12 do you get?   *4 × 3.*
How many jumps if you jump to 12 by 2s?   What factor pair of 12 do you get?   *6 × 2.*

Like all numbers, 12 is a multiple of all its factors. (Discuss. Illustrate.)

Common Factor

Guided Discovery

Referring to two numbers that have a common factor, students need to experience that:
- They **both** belong to the series we get when counting by that common factor.
- The **difference** between the two numbers also shares that common factor.
- The common factor of two numbers can **never be greater than their difference.**

| Count in writing from 1 to 24. |

1 2 ③ 4 5 ⑥ 7 8 ⑨ 10 11 ⑫ 13 14 ⑮ 16 17 ⑱ 19 20 ㉑ 22 23 ㉔

| Circle the multiples of 3. Then, pointing with your finger, count by 3s from 3 to 24: |

| 6 and 21. Fill in with common factor and factor pairs: |

$$\frac{2 \quad 6 \quad 3 \quad 21 \quad 7}{}$$

| 6 and 21 have 3 as a common factor. Are 6 and 21 circled on your list? | *Yes.*

When two numbers such as 6 and 21 have a common factor (3) they **both** belong to the series of numbers we get when we count by that common factor.

| Put an index finger on two multiples of 3.
 Is the difference also a multiple of 3? |

The **difference** between two multiples of a number is also a multiple of that number.

| Choose two multiples of 9. Is their difference a multiple of 9? | *45 − 27 = 18.*
 (5 × 9) − (3 × 9) = 2 × 9.

| 42 and 48 are multiples of 6. Can there be another common factor greater than 6? |

No. The difference is 6. If 13 was a common factor, starting on 42 and counting by 13s, I would skip over 48. A common factor cannot be greater than the difference.

| 376 and 378 are even. Do they have a factor in common?
 Can they have another common factor greater than 2? Why not? | *2*

The Common Factor of two numbers cannot be greater than their difference.

Greatest Common Factor (GCF)

Guided Discovery

Generally, when we look for the common factor between two numbers, we want the Greatest Common Factor (GCF, also called Greatest Common Divisor). After all, 1 is a factor that all numbers have in common. 2 is factor common to all even numbers. These factors are obvious and not much help. We want the GREATEST.

How can we tell we have the GREATEST Common Factor?

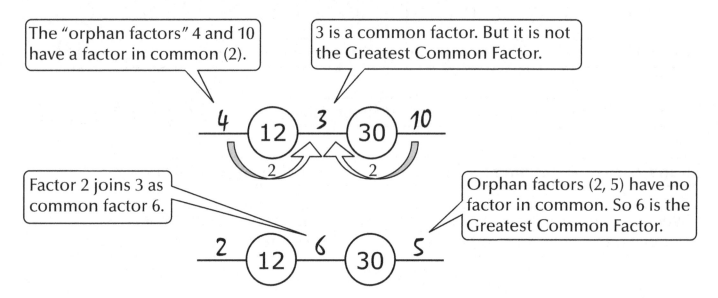

The "orphan factors" 4 and 10 have a factor in common (2).

3 is a common factor. But it is not the Greatest Common Factor.

Factor 2 joins 3 as common factor 6.

Orphan factors (2, 5) have no factor in common. So 6 is the Greatest Common Factor.

Greatest Common Factor and Fractions.

We can only simplify a fraction when numerator and denominator have a common factor.

Example: (Still using 12 and 30 as above.)

If we simplify by a common factor that is not the greatest, the simplified fraction can still be simplified.

The fraction is in simplest form only if we simplify it by the Greatest Common Factor.

$$\frac{12}{30} = \frac{\cancel{3} \times 4}{\cancel{3} \times 10} = \frac{4}{10} = \frac{\cancel{2} \times 2}{\cancel{2} \times 5} = \frac{2}{5}$$

$$\frac{12}{30} = \frac{\cancel{6} \times 2}{\cancel{6} \times 5} = \frac{2}{5}$$

Greatest Common Factor

Here, we chose for you a common factor that is **not** the Greatest Common Factor.
(Notice how the orphan factors still have a factor in common.)
Complete the factor pairs using the given factor. Then correct to find the GCF.

9—(27)—**3**—(18)—**6**

3—(27)—**9**—(18)—**2**

——(24)—**3**—(18)——

——(24)——(18)——

——(18)—**9**—(72)——

——(18)——(72)——

——(32)—**8**—(48)——

——(32)——(48)——

——(63)—**7**—(42)——

——(63)——(42)——

——(24)—**3**—(30)——

——(24)——(30)——

——(16)—**4**—(24)——

——(16)——(24)——

——(12)—**3**—(18)——

——(12)——(18)——

——(54)—**9**—(81)——

——(54)——(81)——

——(70)—**7**—(42)——

——(70)——(42)——

Simplifying Fractions

Guided Discovery

Common factor and factor pairs: A familiar diagram:

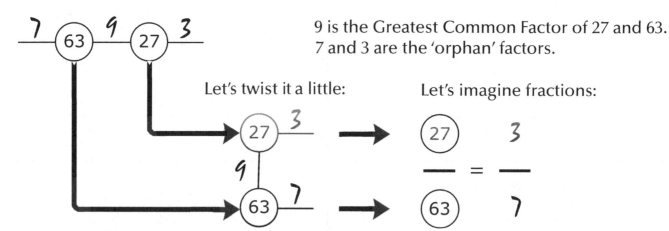

9 is the Greatest Common Factor of 27 and 63. 7 and 3 are the 'orphan' factors.

Let's twist it a little:

Let's imagine fractions:

$$\frac{27}{63} = \frac{3}{7}$$

Fraction 3/7 (the two orphan factors) is the simplified version of fraction 27/63.

> The familiar common factor diagram using 2 bubbles tells us what we need to know to simplify fractions and helps us find the best common denominator to add two fractions.

Find Greatest Common Factor and factor pairs. Simplify the corresponding fraction.

7 —(27)— 9 —(63)— 3 $\dfrac{27}{63} = \dfrac{3}{7}$	—(21)—(49)— $\dfrac{21}{49} = $ —
—(15)—(24)— $\dfrac{15}{24} = $ —	—(35)—(56)— $\dfrac{35}{56} = $ —
—(14)—(21)— $\dfrac{14}{21} = $ —	—(36)—(63)— $\dfrac{36}{63} = $ —
—(32)—(56)— $\dfrac{32}{56} = $ —	—(28)—(49)— $\dfrac{28}{49} = $ —

We can only simplify fractions when numerator and denominator have a common factor. If the common factor used is not the greatest, the simplified fraction can still be simplified.

Simplifying Fractions

> The few pages that follow use simplifying fractions as an opportunity to review essential multiplication facts.

Make sure students can explain in their own words the logic of the simplifying process:

Crossing out 2 in the numerator makes the fraction 2 times smaller: (3/8 instead of 6/8.)

We have fewer parts (3, not 6) but each part is twice as large (1/4, not 1/8.)

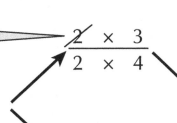

$$\frac{6}{8} = \frac{2 \times 3}{2 \times 4}$$

$$\frac{\cancel{2} \times 3}{2 \times 4}$$

$$\frac{2 \times 3}{\cancel{2} \times 4}$$

$$\frac{\cancel{2} \times 3}{\cancel{2} \times 4} = \frac{3}{4}$$

Crossing out 2 in the denominator makes the fraction 2 times larger: (6/4 instead of 6/8.)

The factors 2 crossed out in both places cancel each other out. The quantity has not changed: 6/8 = 3/4.

Write numerator and denominator as factor pairs showing the Greatest Common Factor. Then, simplify as in model. The Greatest Common Factor can be two-digit number!

$$\frac{56}{64} = \frac{7 \times \cancel{8}}{8 \times \cancel{8}} = \frac{7}{8}$$

$$\frac{49}{70} = \frac{\quad \times \quad}{\quad \times \quad} = \underline{\quad}$$

$$\frac{28}{63} = \frac{\quad \times \quad}{\quad \times \quad} = \underline{\quad}$$

$$\frac{16}{40} = \frac{\quad \times \quad}{\quad \times \quad} = \underline{\quad}$$

$$\frac{36}{42} = \frac{\quad \times \quad}{\quad \times \quad} = \underline{\quad}$$

$$\frac{18}{63} = \frac{\quad \times \quad}{\quad \times \quad} = \underline{\quad}$$

$$\frac{12}{28} = \frac{\quad \times \quad}{\quad \times \quad} = \underline{\quad}$$

$$\frac{27}{63} = \frac{\quad \times \quad}{\quad \times \quad} = \underline{\quad}$$

$$\frac{64}{72} = \frac{\quad \times \quad}{\quad \times \quad} = \underline{\quad}$$

$$\frac{63}{72} = \frac{\quad \times \quad}{\quad \times \quad} = \underline{\quad}$$

Simplifying Fractions

Write numerator and denominator as factor pairs showing the Greatest Common Factor. Then, simplify as in model.

$\dfrac{30}{48}$ = $\dfrac{5 \times \cancel{6}}{\cancel{6} \times 8}$ = $\dfrac{5}{8}$ $\dfrac{21}{24}$ = $\dfrac{\quad \times \quad}{\quad \times \quad}$ = $\underline{\quad}$

$\dfrac{72}{81}$ = $\dfrac{\quad \times \quad}{\quad \times \quad}$ = $\underline{\quad}$ $\dfrac{35}{49}$ = $\dfrac{\quad \times \quad}{\quad \times \quad}$ = $\underline{\quad}$

$\dfrac{27}{72}$ = $\dfrac{\quad \times \quad}{\quad \times \quad}$ = $\underline{\quad}$ $\dfrac{56}{63}$ = $\dfrac{\quad \times \quad}{\quad \times \quad}$ = $\underline{\quad}$

$\dfrac{18}{42}$ = $\dfrac{\quad \times \quad}{\quad \times \quad}$ = $\underline{\quad}$ $\dfrac{63}{72}$ = $\dfrac{\quad \times \quad}{\quad \times \quad}$ = $\underline{\quad}$

$\dfrac{25}{45}$ = $\dfrac{\quad \times \quad}{\quad \times \quad}$ = $\underline{\quad}$ $\dfrac{32}{40}$ = $\dfrac{\quad \times \quad}{\quad \times \quad}$ = $\underline{\quad}$

    $\dfrac{28}{36}$ = $\dfrac{\quad \times \quad}{\quad \times \quad}$ = $\underline{\quad}$

$\dfrac{36}{42}$ = $\dfrac{\quad \times \quad}{\quad \times \quad}$ = $\underline{\quad}$ $\dfrac{49}{63}$ = $\dfrac{\quad \times \quad}{\quad \times \quad}$ = $\underline{\quad}$

$\dfrac{9}{30}$ = $\dfrac{\quad \times \quad}{\quad \times \quad}$ = $\underline{\quad}$ $\dfrac{14}{18}$ = $\dfrac{\quad \times \quad}{\quad \times \quad}$ = $\underline{\quad}$

$\dfrac{21}{35}$ = $\dfrac{\quad \times \quad}{\quad \times \quad}$ = $\underline{\quad}$ $\dfrac{15}{21}$ = $\dfrac{\quad \times \quad}{\quad \times \quad}$ = $\underline{\quad}$

Simplifying Fractions

As you simplify these fractions, instead of showing the factor pairs, use a shortcut.

Write the common factor inside the bubble.

Complete the factor pairs in your mind.

In your mind, check that the proportions make sense, that the ratio of 27 and 45 seems consistent with the ratio of 3 and 5.

$$\frac{27}{45} = ⑨ \frac{3}{5}$$

3 because $27 = 9 \times 3$

5 because $45 = 9 \times 5$

$$\frac{14}{63} = ⑦ \frac{2}{9}$$ $$\frac{8}{12} = ④ ____$$ $$\frac{15}{40} = ⑤ ____$$ $$\frac{24}{40} = ⑧ ____$$

$$\frac{21}{35} = \bigcirc ____$$ $$\frac{18}{63} = \bigcirc ____$$ $$\frac{42}{48} = \bigcirc ____$$ $$\frac{12}{15} = \bigcirc ____$$

$$\frac{49}{56} = \bigcirc ____$$ $$\frac{12}{16} = \bigcirc ____$$ $$\frac{14}{18} = \bigcirc ____$$ $$\frac{9}{21} = \bigcirc ____$$

$$\frac{32}{36} = \bigcirc ____$$ $$\frac{16}{56} = \bigcirc ____$$ $$\frac{8}{18} = \bigcirc ____$$ $$\frac{35}{42} = \bigcirc ____$$

$$\frac{25}{45} = \bigcirc ____$$ $$\frac{16}{20} = \bigcirc ____$$ $$\frac{16}{24} = \bigcirc ____$$ $$\frac{54}{63} = \bigcirc ____$$

$$\frac{56}{64} = \bigcirc ____$$ $$\frac{35}{42} = \bigcirc ____$$ $$\frac{18}{30} = \bigcirc ____$$ $$\frac{40}{70} = \bigcirc ____$$

$$\frac{6}{15} = \bigcirc ____$$ $$\frac{9}{24} = \bigcirc ____$$ $$\frac{14}{20} = \bigcirc ____$$ $$\frac{21}{28} = \bigcirc ____$$

Simplifying Fractions

Show the common factor in the bubble. Then simplify.

$\dfrac{28}{36}$ ④ $= \dfrac{7 \;(4 \times 7)}{9 \;(4 \times 9)}$ $\dfrac{21}{56}$ ◯ $=$ ____ $\dfrac{40}{72}$ ◯ $=$ ____

$\dfrac{50}{80}$ ◯ $=$ ____ $\dfrac{45}{72}$ ◯ $=$ ____ $\dfrac{15}{27}$ ◯ $=$ ____ $\dfrac{35}{63}$ ◯ $=$ ____

$\dfrac{28}{63}$ ◯ $=$ ____ $\dfrac{12}{40}$ ◯ $=$ ____ $\dfrac{63}{81}$ ◯ $=$ ____ $\dfrac{56}{64}$ ◯ $=$ ____

$\dfrac{27}{63}$ ◯ $=$ ____ $\dfrac{9}{15}$ ◯ $=$ ____ $\dfrac{14}{49}$ ◯ $=$ ____ $\dfrac{16}{72}$ ◯ $=$ ____

$\dfrac{24}{64}$ ◯ $=$ ____ $\dfrac{24}{30}$ ◯ $=$ ____ $\dfrac{14}{18}$ ◯ $=$ ____ $\dfrac{15}{21}$ ◯ $=$ ____

- -

$\dfrac{32}{56}$ ◯ $=$ ____ $\dfrac{45}{72}$ ◯ $=$ ____ $\dfrac{16}{36}$ ◯ $=$ ____ $\dfrac{27}{72}$ ◯ $=$ ____

$\dfrac{9}{54}$ ⑨ $=$ ____ $\dfrac{14}{21}$ ◯ $=$ ____ $\dfrac{28}{63}$ ◯ $=$ ____ $\dfrac{42}{48}$ ◯ $=$ ____

$\dfrac{63}{81}$ ◯ $=$ ____ $\dfrac{49}{56}$ ◯ $=$ ____ $\dfrac{14}{63}$ ◯ $=$ ____ $\dfrac{36}{42}$ ◯ $=$ ____

$\dfrac{16}{36}$ ◯ $=$ ____ $\dfrac{36}{81}$ ◯ $=$ ____ $\dfrac{40}{70}$ ◯ $=$ ____ $\dfrac{21}{27}$ ◯ $=$ ____

Least Common Multiple (1)

Guided Discovery

> A bell rings every 6 minutes.
> Circle the times when it rings. They are all multiples of 6.

1 2 3 4 5 ⑥ 7 8 9 10 11 ⑫ 13 14 15 16 17 ⑱ 19 20 21 22 23 ㉔ 25
↕ Minutes
1 2 3 4 5 6 7 ⑧ 9 10 11 12 13 14 15 ⑯ 17 18 19 20 21 22 23 ㉔ 25

> Another bell rings every 8 minutes.
> Circle the times when it rings. They are all multiples of 8.

> 24 is a multiple of 6 and of 8.

> The two bells start ringing at the same time.
> When do they ring again at the same time for the first time?

24 minutes after the first ring. This is the first number that is circled on both lines.

> 24 is a multiple of 6 and of 8. It is the first multiple that 6 and 8 have in common.
> It is the LEAST COMMON MULTIPLE (LCM) of 6 and 8.

LEAST means **smallest.** Think: *"LESS."* Think: *"The LEAST you can give him for his birthday is $20.00."* You can give more but not less. Multiples can be as large as we want. We are often interested in the **smallest** one: the LEAST COMMON MULTIPLE or LCM.

> How often do they ring again at the same time?

Every 24 minutes.

> Do they ring at the same time after 240 minutes? Why?
> After 24,024 minutes?   Why?

It is a multiple of 24.
It is a multiple of 24.

How to find the Least Common Multiple of two numbers?

1. With simple numbers you can count by one of the numbers until you recognize a multiple of the other one:

> Find the LCM of 6 and 8:

"6…12…18…24. Ah! That's also a multiple of 8!"

2. There is a better approach that uses the Greatest Common Factor (GCF) to find the Least Common Multiple (LCM). (See next page.)

Guided Discovery

Familiar common factor and factor pairs:

$$2 \quad \textcircled{12} \quad 6 \quad \textcircled{42} \quad 7$$

| Multiply the three factors, common factor 6 and "orphan" factors 2 and 7. |

$$2 \quad \times \quad 6 \quad \times \quad 7 \quad = \quad 84$$

| Is 84 a multiple of 12? |

Yes, 12 x 7

$$\overline{2 \quad \times \quad 6} \quad \times \quad 7 \quad = \quad 84$$

$$\textcircled{12} \qquad \times \quad 7 \quad = \quad 84$$

| Is 84 a multiple of 42? |

Yes, 2 x 42

$$2 \quad \times \quad \overline{6 \quad \times \quad 7} \quad = \quad 84$$

$$2 \quad \times \quad \textcircled{42} \qquad = \quad 84$$

| Common factor 6 does double duty: |

$$\overline{2 \quad \times \quad \overline{6} \quad \times \quad 7} \quad = \quad 84$$

| To find 84, we have a choice:
Which is the easier to multiply: 12 × 7 or 2 × 42? |

Probably 2 × 42?

| How do we know that 84 is the
LEAST Common Multiple of 12 and 42? |

*'Orphan' factors 2 and 7 do
not have a common factor.*

Least Common Multiple and Fractions:

When adding two fractions that have 12 and 42 as denominators (Ex.: 5/12 + 11/42),
Least Common Multiple 84 is the best option as the new common denominator.

$$\frac{5}{12} + \frac{11}{42} \;=\; \frac{5 \times 7}{12 \times 7} + \frac{11 \times 2}{42 \times 2} \;=\; \frac{35 + 22}{84} \;=\; \frac{57}{84}$$

$$2 \times \overline{6} \times 7$$

| Our ability to see 2 × 6 × 7 as 12 × 7 helps us multiply denominator and numerator of 5/12 by 7: 5/12 = 35/84. | Our ability to see 2 × 6 × 7 as 2 × 42 helps us multiply denominator and numerator of 11/42 by 2: 11/42 = 22/84. | We now have two equivalent fractions (35/84 and 22/84) with a common denominator. They can now be added. |

Least Common Multiple (LCM) 3-35

GCF — LCM

2 (14) 7 (21) 3

2 × 7 × 3 = 42

2 × 7 × 3 = 42

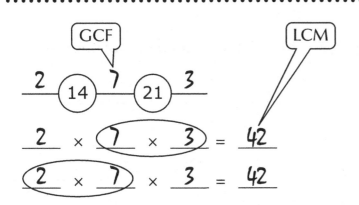

To multiply the three factors, choose the easier option: 2 × 21 is easier than 14 × 3.

2 × (21) = 42

(14) × 3 = 42

Find the Least Common Multiple. Show your choice of which two numbers you multiply.

2 (8) 4 (12) 3 2 × (12) = 24	7 (49) 7 (21) 3 (49) × 3 = 147
(14) (35) ____ × ____ = ____	(30) (70) ____ × ____ = ____
(63) (18) ____ × ____ = ____	(56) (14) ____ × ____ = ____
(21) (56) ____ × ____ = ____	(50) (15) ____ × ____ = ____
(28) (35) ____ × ____ = ____	(18) (45) ____ × ____ = ____

Least Common Multiple (LCM)

Find the Least Common Multiple. Show your choice of which two numbers you multiply.

$\underline{\quad 3 \quad}$ (21) $\underline{\quad 7 \quad}$ (14) $\underline{\quad 2 \quad}$

$\underline{\quad (21) \quad} \times \underline{\quad 2 \quad} = \underline{\quad 42 \quad}$

---

(64) —— (16)

$\underline{\qquad} \times \underline{\qquad} = \underline{\qquad}$

---

(15) —— (21)

$\underline{\qquad} \times \underline{\qquad} = \underline{\qquad}$

---

(27) —— (81)

$\underline{\qquad} \times \underline{\qquad} = \underline{\qquad}$

---

(36) —— (27)

$\underline{\qquad} \times \underline{\qquad} = \underline{\qquad}$

---

(56) —— (16)

$\underline{\qquad} \times \underline{\qquad} = \underline{\qquad}$

---

(42) —— (30)

$\underline{\qquad} \times \underline{\qquad} = \underline{\qquad}$

---

(36) —— (28)

$\underline{\qquad} \times \underline{\qquad} = \underline{\qquad}$

---

(35) —— (14)

$\underline{\qquad} \times \underline{\qquad} = \underline{\qquad}$

---

(25) —— (10)

$\underline{\qquad} \times \underline{\qquad} = \underline{\qquad}$

---

(54) —— (45)

$\underline{\qquad} \times \underline{\qquad} = \underline{\qquad}$

---

(63) —— (49)

$\underline{\qquad} \times \underline{\qquad} = \underline{\qquad}$

---

(12) —— (30)

$\underline{\qquad} \times \underline{\qquad} = \underline{\qquad}$

---

(6) —— (21)

$\underline{\qquad} \times \underline{\qquad} = \underline{\qquad}$

Least Common Multiple (LCM) 3-37 ⊞

Use the Greatest Common Factor to find the Least Common Multiple, as in model.

3 ─(27)─ 9 ─(45)─ 5   5 ─(30)─ 6 ─(12)─ 2

3 × (45) = 135   (30) × 2 = 60

─(10)──(35)─   ─(12)──(40)─

___ × ___ = ___   ___ × ___ = ___

─(9)──(21)─   ─(54)──(42)─

___ × ___ = ___   ___ × ___ = ___

─(18)──(24)─   ─(80)──(24)─

___ × ___ = ___   ___ × ___ = ___

─(15)──(25)─   ─(16)──(24)─

___ × ___ = ___   ___ × ___ = ___

─(28)──(21)─

___ × ___ = ___

I've got It!

I deserve to be congratulated.

─(63)──(35)─   ─(42)──(14)─

___ × ___ = ___   ___ × ___ = ___

3-38(1) ⊞

Fill in all the cells:
Factors from 2 to 10
in grey cells;
Corresponding products
in white cells.

> What factor
> do 15, 24 and 21
> have in common?

	3			9			10	2
7								
		60						
	27							
					18			
8								
			15	24		21		
	15						50	
		36				24		
4								

3-38(2) ⊞

		10							
									12
			54					24	
							25		
10									
			18						
			63						
	54			63	18	72			27
			27						
			72						

Factor Chain

Show **common factors** and **factor pairs**.
Use only factors from 2 to 9.

> The Factor Chains and Messed-Up Times Squares that follow can be assigned at any time while students are studying any Level 3 material.

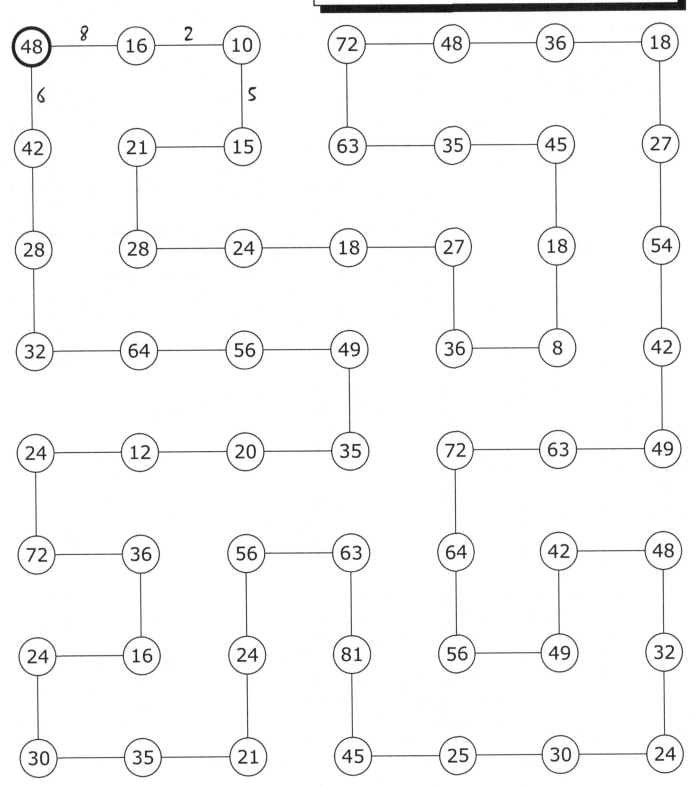

Messed-Up Times Squares

3-40(1) ▦

Fill in all the cells:
Factors from 2 to 10 in grey cells;
Corresponding products in white cells.

		3					9	10	
					72				
					40				
		12							
			60						
	40			56		16			32
		18							
			12	14			18		
					56				
					24				

3-40(2) ▦

	2		3				5		
				54				63	
4						16			
					45				50
8			30						
2									20
						28			
6		48							
							15		

Factor Chain

Show **common factors** and **factor pairs**.
Use only factors from 2 to 9.

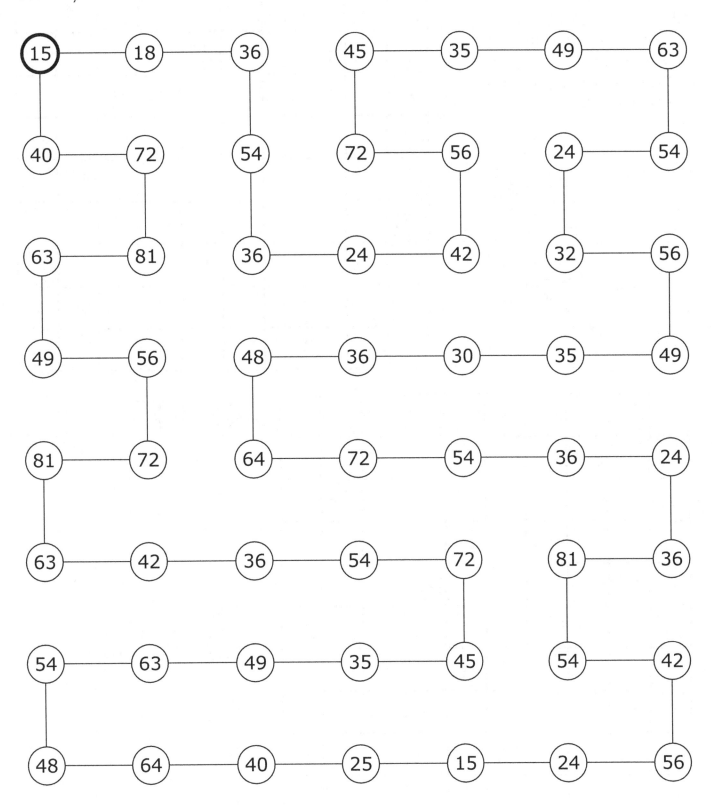

Messed-Up Times Squares

3-42(1)

Fill in all the cells:
Factors from 2 to 10
in grey cells;
Corresponding products
in white cells.

	9			6				
			20				14	
		56			21			
4							8	
						36		45
							42	
10								
					9			
							56	
5								

3-42(2)

			6					
	64							
						49		
		36		16				
				100				
							25	
				36				
	9							
			36					
					4			

Option:
Keep remaining Level 3
pages for future review.

Factor Chain

Show **common factors** and **factor pairs**.
Use only factors from 2 to 9.

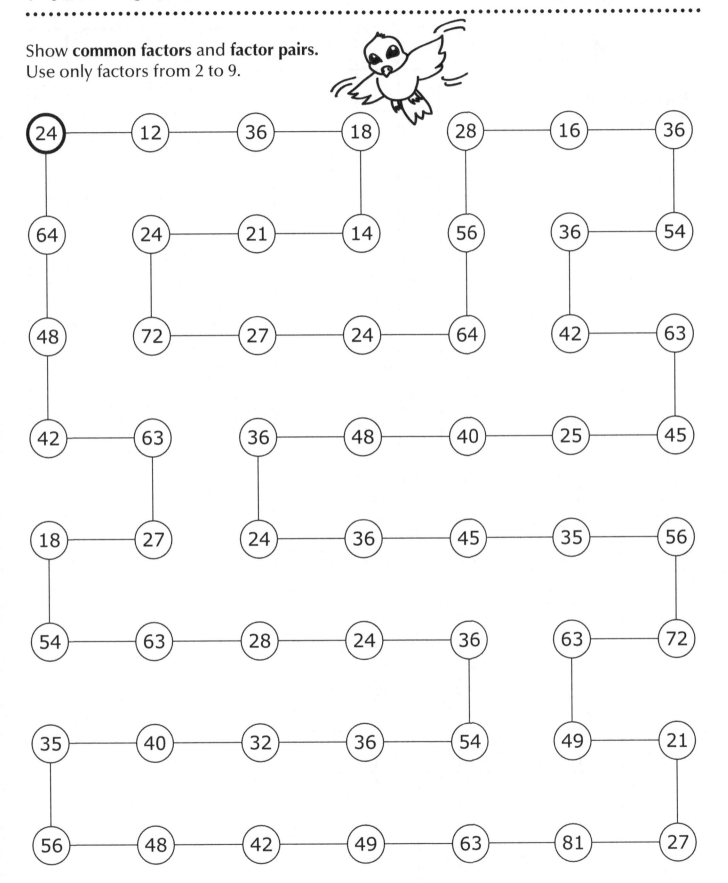

Messed-Up Times Squares

3-44(1)

Fill in all the cells:
Factors from 2 to 10
in grey cells;
Corresponding products
in white cells.

						64			80
					9				
				49				42	
			25						
		81							
	4								
								36	
					30				
	8						16		

3-44(2)

	36						32		
		36							
6			36						
				35				14	
	45				35				
					56	24			
	100								
		8							
				21					

Factor Chain

Show **common factors** and **factor pairs**.
Use only factors from 2 to 9.

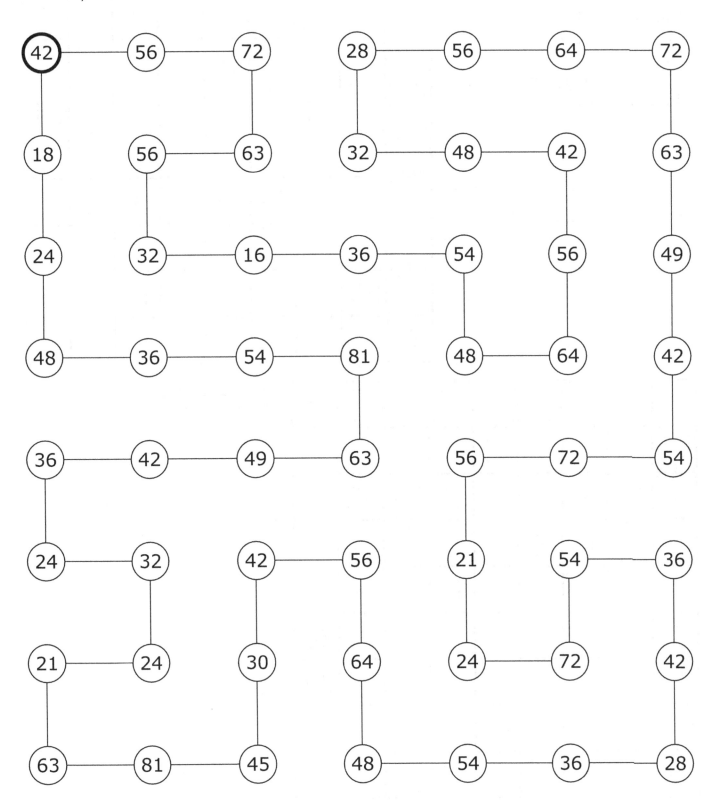

Messed-Up Times Squares

3-46 (1)

Fill in all the cells:
Factors from 2 to 9
in grey cells;
Corresponding products
in white cells.

							5	
						4		
			64	32				
	81							54
					8			
		21	56					
	27			12				
	35				10			
6								

3-46 (2)

							9
		63					
				14	42		
	16	6					
			15	6			
16						36	
						72	
		42		12			
	15						

Factor Chain

Show **common factors** and **factor pairs.**
Use only factors from 2 to 9.

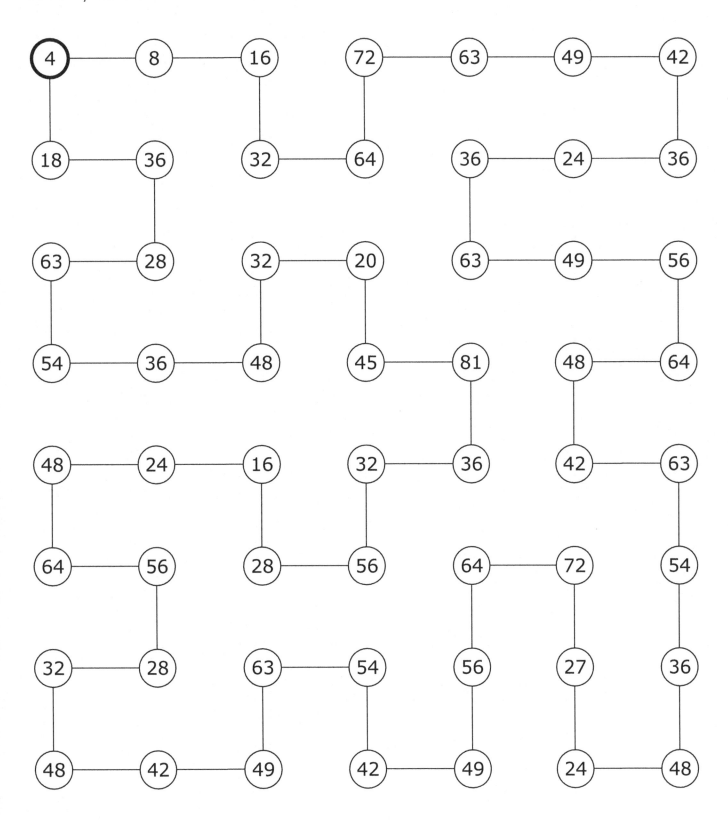

Made in the USA
Middletown, DE
01 April 2021